PLACEBOS
AND THE
PHILOSOPHY
OF MEDICINE

PLACEBOS

AND THE

PHILOSOPHY

OF MEDICINE

*Clinical, Conceptual, and
Ethical Issues*

Howard Brody, M.D.

THE UNIVERSITY OF CHICAGO PRESS

CHICAGO AND LONDON

The University of Chicago Press, Chicago 60637
The University of Chicago Press, Ltd., London
© 1977, 1980 by The University of Chicago
All rights reserved. Published 1980
Printed in the United States of America
84 83 82 81 80   5 4 3 2 1

Howard Brody was educated at Michigan State
University, where he received his M.D. in 1976 and
his Ph.D. in philosophy in 1977. He is currently
a resident in family practice at the University of
Virginia Medical Center.

LIBRARY OF CONGRESS CATALOGING IN PUBLICATION DATA

Brody, Howard.
  Placebos and the philosophy of medicine.

  Revision of the author's thesis, Michigan State
University, 1977.
  Bibliography: p.
  Includes index.
  1. Medicine—Philosophy. 2. Placebo
(Medicine) 3. Mind and body. I. Title.
[DNLM: 1. Placebos. 2. Ethics, Medical.
3. Philosophy, Medical. WB330 B864p]
R723.B68 1980   610'.1   79–18481
ISBN 0–226–07531–1

Contents

140902

Acknowledgments

The research and preparation of the dissertation on which this book is based was supported by a fellowship from the Institute on Human Values in Medicine, Philadelphia, financed by National Endowment for the Humanities Grant no. EH–10973–74–365. While I appreciate this financial support, I am especially grateful for the advice and encouragement from Institute directors and staff, including Thomas K. McElhinney, Ph.D., Edmund D. Pellegrino, M. D., and Ronald W. McNeur, Ph.D.

The most gratifying feature of completing this work was the opportunity to engage the intellects of a spirited and enthusiastic dissertation committee—Joseph F. Hanna, Ph.D., and Martin Benjamin, Ph.D., of the Department of Philosophy; and William B. Weil, Jr., M.D., and James E. Trosko, Ph.D., of the Department of Human Development, College of Human Medicine.

Helpful ideas were contributed by many people too numerous to mention, at Michigan State University and elsewhere; among those kind enough to suggest references or lines of inquiry were Arthur F. Kohrman, David S. Sobel, Joseph Margolis, Arthur Kleinman, Peter Vinten-Johansen, Donald A. Kennedy, and Sumer Verma.

Introduction

Philosophical Dimensions
of the Placebo Effect

Physicians have known for at least several centuries that patients often display marked improvement of symptoms when given a sugar pill, or some other substance having no known medicinal properties, under the impression that it is an active drug. A biomedically inert substance given in such a manner to produce relief is known as a *placebo,* and the resulting effect upon the patient may be called the *placebo effect.* With the advent of large-scale clinical trials of drugs and therapeutics during the past three decades, placebos have become an important way of eliminating investigator bias in medical research design. As a result, a good deal has been learned about the placebo effect in the course of studying other therapies, and this in turn has directly stimulated study of the placebo effect. As investigators have come to learn more about psychosomatic medicine and about psychological and social determinants of disease, they have attempted to develop a comprehensive psychophysiological theory capable of explaining the placebo effect.

These developments in medicine raise three major philosophical issues. First, physicians have not devoted much attention to rigorously defining what is meant by *placebo effect* and to delineating the sorts of phenomena to which it is intended to apply. This task is a difficult one because much remains to be learned about the placebo effect. On the one hand, one wants a definition specific enough to serve as a helpful guide in laying out research strategies. On the other hand, one wants a definition general enough so that it does not treat matters which ought to be settled empirically as conceptual issues to be settled a priori. Several points in the philosophy of science, including the question of what counts as an adequate explanation and how one establishes the truth of scientific theories, must be taken into account in seeking this balance.

Second, what is known about the placebo effect suggests that a patient's beliefs or expectations can in some way influence his bodily states. This appears to have implications for the relationship between mind and body: some philosophical views of the mind-body relation allow for such a connection whereas others do not.

Third, the actual use of placebos by physicians in therapeutic encounters raises ethical issues—specifically, issues within that area of normative ethics which is becoming known as *medical ethics*.

Each of these three sets of issues can be dealt with in straightforward fashion by the philosophical approaches already mentioned. We might arrive at a formal definition of *placebo effect,* for example, by looking at how the words are actually used by investigators in the field, or by looking at the operational methods employed to measure it. We might adapt an existing mind-body view, such as Cartesian causal interactionism, to give an account of the placebo effect in mind-body terms. And we can handle the ethical issues within either the utilitarian or the deontological framework as a subcategory of cases involving deception. In this way all the issues might be settled, each in isolation from the others.

It is both more challenging and more satisfying, however, to aim for a more comprehensive approach. We would like to arrive at a formal definition of *placebo effect* which not only takes care of narrowly empirical issues, but also illuminates the tasks of investigating the mind-body relation and of framing an ethical argument. And we would like to find a mind-body theory that not only accounts for the existence of the placebo effect, but also helps us to understand it further in terms of its definition and its ethical import. That is, the philosophical accounts given in response to the three sets of issues ought to be not only plausible when taken singly, but also mutually consistent and illuminating when taken together.

We also demand more. In each of these three areas we already have what we may call considered judgments, many of which have little or nothing to do with the placebo effect. In the empirical realm we know, for instance, that a sugar pill, according to existing pharmacologic theories, has no medicinal properties so far as its chemical structure is concerned. In the area of mind and body, we know that we have minds—that we are conscious of ourselves and our surroundings in a way that trees and rocks are not, and in a way that animals may share to some degree. And in the normative realm we know that it is wrong to torture others for our own amusement. These are the sorts of things we are certain of if we can claim to be certain of anything at all; we are confident that we are not led to believe these things simply because we are confused, or because we are biased by selfish interests (Rawls 1971, pp. 47–48). Therefore, we would be reluctant to adopt a mind-body theory or an ethical stance which conflicted with these considered judgments, just because this seemed a neat, ad hoc way out of a specific dilemma raised by the placebo case. Thus the degree of overall fit we ideally aim for among our three philosophical theories and our three types of considered judgments is extensive, and the chances are that we will never get a perfect fit but only a workable approximation. And even this approximation may be upset by new discoveries or by new types of cases which cause us to rethink our ethical positions.[1]

We can summarize this approach schematically. Let C and C' be two alternative conceptual theories for organizing the empirical data about the placebo effect. Let M and M' be two alternative metaphysical theories about the mind-body relation, and let N and N' be two alternative normative theories (of moral obligation). Also, let $c_1, c_2, \ldots, c_n, m_1, m_2, \ldots, m_n$, and $n_1, n_2, \ldots, n_n$ represent our considered judgments about conceptual-empirical, metaphysical mind-body, and normative matters, respectively, all of which are independent of our beliefs about the placebo effect. Now, if all of the following are true,

1. C and C', M and M', and N and N' are each equally plausible insofar as they are able to explain the relevant features of the placebo effect, taken in isolation,

2. Taken together, (C, M, N) is internally more consistent than (C', M, N), (C, M', N), (C, M, N'), (C', M', N), or any other combination,

3. C is more consistent with $c_1, c_2, \ldots, c_n$ than is C', M is more consistent with $m_1, m_2, \ldots, m_n$ than is M', and N is more consistent with n_1, $n_2, \ldots, n_n$ than is N',

then we would have the strongest possible grounds for preferring C, M, and N over C', M', and N', respectively. Furthermore, even if C were slightly less plausible than C' when applied to the placebo effect in isolation, we might be willing to trade this off against the much greater degree of overall fit offered by the set of the theories (C, M, N), and the agreement with existing considered judgments on other matters of philosophical importance.[2]

The approach just described arises from a particular preconception of philosophy in general, which also turns out to have important applications to the new subdiscipline of philosophy which is becoming known as *philosophy of medicine*.[3] On this view, we engage in philosophy in order to find a more intelligible and coherent view of the world, including our own places in the world. Technical precision in philosophy is desirable and advantageous for this and other reasons, but by itself precision does not satisfy the basic need for comprehensive understanding which leads us to philosophy initially. Where a conflict arises, we may be willing to dispense with a certain amount of technical precision to satisfy this need. Furthermore, since knowing our own places in the world requires us to see ourselves often as agents rather than always as spectators, we must find a place for morality as well as metaphysics in the world view we are constructing. We are not content to know about other people and situations in a merely descriptive way; we want to know how we ought to act toward others in particular situations. Specifically, we want to avoid any metaphysical theory (such as a crude determinism), however intriguing it may be empirically, that seems to leave no room for free actions and moral thinking.[4]

This preconception of philosophy seems especially applicable to the philosophy of medicine. An increased emphasis on technical precision has taken medicine a long way, but precision has been shown to have its limits, and what reflective physicians have always referred to as the *art* of medicine continues to defy precise analysis.

The phrase *art of medicine* can, of course, invite misuse. Practitioners have used the phrase to cover up a good deal of muddled thinking and uncritically accepted prejudices. The term is perhaps most misleading when applied to aspects of medical practice which are amenable to empirical study but about which sufficient data have not yet been accumulated. Physicians in fact commonly use the word *philosophy* in such contexts: "My philosophy on using decongestants for chronic serous otitis is...." Implicit in such usage is the erroneous assumption that what has been labeled a matter of art or philosophy is thereby exempt from rigorous evaluation.

But the term *art* may be appropriately applied to aspects of medicine which serve to demonstrate that medicine can never be reduced to an empirical science. One may call attention to certain inherent limitations in medicine, such as the fact that the practitioner must *in principle* always act from an incomplete data base. Or one may call attention to the fact that medical activities necessarily involve us in value choices and may call into question our views of ourselves, of our mortality, and of our humanity.

Thus medicine necessarily crosses all the boundaries that we have tried to draw between the empirical, the metaphysical, and the moral realms. Medicine, above all other fields of study, refuses to let any of us remain spectators for long. The physician cannot merely observe and describe the course of disease; he must intervene actively, in a way that has dramatic impact on the rights and interests of other people. And the physician himself is liable at any moment to switch roles and become the patient.[5] When medicine is viewed in this way, the issues raised by the placebo effect are seen to epitomize the philosophy of medicine as a whole.

The view of philosophy stated above requires some additional comment. The notions of *overall fit* and *equal plausibility*, for instance, require considerable amplification if the account is to be defended against possible criticisms. I certainly do not intend the notion of *fit* to be so strong as to suggest mutual logical entailment among C, M, and N. But I think that the notions of *fit* and *plausibility*, as they will be employed below, can be understood intuitively; this at least will allow the account to serve as a rough guide for the investigation. The best way to amplify this intuitive level of understanding is actually to carry out the investigation and then to enumerate the points of carry-over and cross-fertilization that have arisen. The account can serve as a rough guide to what follows even though all steps in the schematic will not be carried out explicitly.

These problems aside, however, anyone committed to the Anglo-American analytic tradition is likely to look suspiciously on any search for a comprehensive philosophical overview in which internal fit is stressed. And, indeed, one could cite examples of imaginative and internally consistent philosophical accounts that are no more than meaningless exercises in fantasy. But the serious flaw in such accounts is not the attempt at comprehensiveness or the value placed on internal fit, but rather the failure to be grounded at any point on an acceptable base, empirical or otherwise. So long as our attempt takes into account our considered judgments, empirical and metaphysical, and moral, there seems little reason to fear that we will be building any castles-in-the-air. Some, of course, would insist that the empirical corner of the *CMN* triangle ought to be given priority over considered judgments of other types; and they should be happy to note that the emphasis on internal fit can be expected to augment the empirical content of the other two corners.

ONE

The Placebo Effect
A Review of the
Medical Literature

Physicians have only recently approached the placebo effect as a subject for formal investigation and speculation. Pepper, in a 1945 paper sometimes considered a classic in this field, admitted that he was unable to find any articles on placebos listed in two major medical bibliographic indexes. Shapiro, a prolific reviewer, states that the recent interest in placebos dates from 1953 and was stimulated by the desire to design adequate double-blind therapeutic trials (1968).[1] Probably the bulk of the medical literature on placebos treats the placebo effect as a nuisance variable, worthy of notice only for the havoc it can wreak upon inadequately designed experiments. Thus one reads, for instance, that psychotherapy will become a more potent tool when it is isolated from the concomitant placebo effect, just as foxglove became a more useful medicine when the active ingredient, digitalis, was extracted (Shapiro 1964). But other writers emphasize the positive therapeutic potential of the placebo effect and the insight it may offer into psychosomatic disease and healing.

This review of the medical literature will consider in turn the history of the term *placebo* and definitions offered for it, the nature and scope of placebo responses, agents that can act as placebos, factors influencing the placebo effect, and explanatory hypotheses that have been proposed.

1.1 HISTORY AND DEFINITION

The word *placebo* entered the English language in the four-teenth century as the name for the vespers sung for the dead (Shapiro 1968). The word was derived from the Latin version of Psalm 116:9: "Placebo Domino in regione vivorum" (Pepper 1945), usually translated "I shall walk before the Lord in the land of the living," although the literal translation of *placebo* is "I shall please." From the original usage the word acquired both its medical application and its negative connotation. Medically, doing something soothing for patient and relatives when nothing curative can be accomplished, might be com-pared to singing a hymn (Osmond 1974). And since in Chaucer's time *placebo* had acquired—from the practice of singing vespers on behalf of strangers for pay (Pepper 1945)—the meaning of sycophant or servile flatterer, the nega-tive association was already well established.

Motherby's New Medical Dictionary (1785) defined *placebo* in neutral and uninformative terms as "a commonplace method or medicine" (Shapiro 1968). By contrast, *Hooper's Medical Dictionary* (1811) derided *placebo* as "an epithet given to any medicine adopted to please rather than to benefit the patient" (Pepper 1945), as if the two were mutually exclu-sive goals.

Contemporary definitions offered by investigators in the field tend to avoid judgmental terms, but still show significant dif-ferences of opinion. Pepper (1945) represents the restrictive end of the spectrum by defining *placebo* as an agent that is totally inert. Presumably he means inert in a pharmacologic sense only; if an agent produced no effect whatsoever one would hardly label it a placebo. Wolf (1959) clarifies this point by defining *placebo effect* as "any effect attributable to a pill, potion, or procedure, but not to its pharmacodynamic or specific properties." A very broad and inclusive definition is suggested by Modell's comment (1955, p. 55) that the *placebo reaction* is "the only single action which all drugs have in common."

Probably the most detailed definition is Shapiro's (1968):

> A *placebo* is defined as any therapy (or that com-
> ponent of any therapy) that is deliberately used for
> its nonspecific psychologic or psychophysiologic
> effect, or that is used for its presumed effect on a
> patient, symptom, or illness, but which, unknown
> to patient and therapist, is without specific activity
> for the condition being treated.
>
> A *placebo,* when used as a control in experimen-
> tal studies, is defined as a substance or procedure
> that is without specific activity for the condition
> being evaluated.
>
> The *placebo effect* is defined as the nonspecific
> psychologic or psychophysiologic effect produced
> by placebos (p. 599).

Shapiro notes that by his definition a *placebo* (1) may be phar-
mocologically inert or active, (2) may or may not produce the
placebo effect in any given instance, (3) may produce effects
that are either positive or negative (i.e., placebo side effects).
The reference to "presumed effect" allows for the notion of
unwitting placebo use by physicians and is the basis for the
often quoted statement, "The history of medical treatment can
be characterized largely as the history of the placebo effect"
(Shapiro 1968, p. 597).

1.2 NATURE AND SCOPE OF RESPONSE

Shapiro (1968) succinctly summarizes the importance and the
breadth of the placebo effect:

> Many papers have demonstrated the importance
> and magnitude of the placebo effect in every
> therapeutic area. Placebos can be more powerful
> than, and reverse the action of, potent active drugs.
> The incidence of placebo reactions approaches 100
> per cent in some studies. Placebos can have pro-
> found effects on organic illnesses, including incur-
> able malignancies. Placebos can often mimic the
> effects of active drugs. Uncontrolled studies of drug

efficacy are reported effective four to five times more frequently than controlled studies. Placebo effects are so omnipresent that if they are not reported in controlled studies it is commonly accepted that the studies are unreliable. Increased appreciation of placebo effects is reflected in the speculation that the major medical achievement of the last decade will be recorded by future medical historians as the development of methodology and controlled experiments (p. 598).[2]

The symptom most often thought of in association with placebos is pain; but placebos modify both subjectively reported and objectively observable symptoms. One reviewer gives the following list of conditions in which placebos have been shown to produce relief: cough, mood changes, angina pectoris, headache, seasickness, anxiety, hypertension, status asthmaticus, depression, and the common cold (Bourne 1971). Placebos can lower blood-sugar levels in diabetics (Singer and Hurwitz 1967) and can shrink tumors in patients with malignant lymphosarcoma (Klopfer 1957). When a subjective symptom and its physiological concomitant (e.g., nausea and disturbed gastric motility) can be observed simultaneously, placebos can be shown to affect both (Wolf 1950).[3]

Placebos can also produce toxic side effects like those of active drugs. One typical study reported the following side effects among twenty-five patients experiencing negative placebo reactions (Honzak, Horackova, and Culik 1972):

Somnolence (10 cases)

Palpitations (9 cases)

Irritability and insomnia (8 cases)

Weakness, with drop in blood pressure of more than
    20 mm mercury (5 cases)

Temporal headache (4 cases)

Diarrhea (3 cases)

Collapse (2 cases)

Itching (2 cases)

In addition, three of these patients developed dependence on the placebo and demonstrated withdrawal symptoms when the pill was stopped. In another study, one patient repeatedly responded to placebo administration by developing a florid rash, diagnosed as classic drug-induced dermatitis by a consulting dermatologist; it ceased immediately upon discontinuance of the placebo, which in this case was plain lactose (Wolf and Pinsky 1954).

Placebo reactions may resemble those of active drugs not only in the end results but also in the patterns of activity. These patterns include a peak effect a certain number of hours after administration of the drug, a cumulative effect of increasing symptom relief as the drug is continued over time, with a carry-over effect after the drug is stopped, and a decrease in efficacy as the severity of the symptom increases. These pharmacologic patterns occur with placebos as well as with active agents (Lasagna, Laties, and Dohan 1958). Some investigators have reported that placebo effects are more transitory than the effects of "real" drugs (Lasagna et al. 1954), but there is enough contrary evidence to question this (Rosenthal and Frank 1956).

1.3 AGENTS ACTING AS PLACEBOS

Essentially any treatment modality can act as a placebo, and patient reactivity will vary according to the supposed potency of the treatment one thinks one is getting. A placebo capsule, in general, is more powerful than a placebo pill, an injection works better than either, and an injection that stings is better than a painless one (Evans 1974). In one study a white or yellow capsule produced the maximal therapeutic effect, while side effects occurred most frequently with a reddish-gray capsule (Honzak, Horackova, and Culik 1972). Surgery is an especially powerful placebo stimulus (Beecher 1961).

It is not always easy to distinguish a placebo stimulus from active therapy. A recent study tried to compare true acupuncture therapy with a sham acupuncture procedure for chronic shoulder pain. The placebo treatment consisted of pricking the skin with acupuncture needles without actually inserting them, and then tapping them on the skin (Moore and Berk 1976). But since cutaneous stimulation of any type may promote pain relief (Melzack and Wall 1965), the sham procedure cannot be considered to be physiologically inactive.

An especially intriguing study was Park and Covi's (1965) nonblind placebo trial. These researchers gave sugar capsules to fifteen outpatients with neurotic complaints, telling them that the pills were sugar and contained no medicine, that such pills had helped other patients in the past, and that the doctors were convinced that the patient would get relief also. Fourteen patients completed a week's trial of therapy, and all but one showed improvement of symptoms by a standard symptom inventory (the remaining patient's husband had made a suicidal gesture during that week).

The patients could be divided into three groups: those certain that the capsule was a placebo, those certain that the capsule was an active drug, and those not certain. The two groups feeling certain either way showed the most improvement. Of the first group, half attributed their improvement to the placebo, and half to their own abilities to cope—one stated that the pill served as a constant reminder that she could do something to improve her own condition. Also, some of these patients were glad to avoid the addiction and overdose potentials of active medication. Among those sure that the placebo was really an active drug, most reasoned that this must be the case since they had improved. They either ignored the sugar-pill explanation, or dismissed it as a therapeutic gimmick of the physician to encourage patient self-sufficiency. Half of those certain that the pill was an active drug reported side effects, while none of those believing that it was a sugar pill did so.

A major flaw in the Park and Covi study (1965) is that the investigators were initially unwilling to offer placebo as the only treatment modality to these new patients seeking help. Therefore they explained that the placebo would be given only for one week and that subsequently other treatment could be considered. This may have had the effect of putting the patients "on probation" for the week, creating thereby a great desire to please the doctors—possibly accounting for the nearly 100 percent placebo response as compared to the more usual 30 to 50 percent response (Beecher 1955). It has also been shown that being on a waiting list to be seen at a psychiatric facility exerts a placebo effect of its own and hastens recovery (Sloane et al. 1975).[4] As more is written about the placebo effect, however, patients will be more likely to conclude that they have received placebos, and this belief may not necessarily hamper their response to therapy (Cousins 1976).

1.4 FACTORS INFLUENCING THE PLACEBO EFFECT

As soon as the importance of the placebo effect began to be understood, investigators began to search for personality factors that would identify the *placebo reactor,* in the hope that eliminating such subjects from controlled studies would produce clearer data. An early study (Lasagna et al. 1954) claimed that the placebo reactor displayed the following characteristics: more outgoing, more anxious, less emotionally mature, more concerned about visceral complaints such as constipation, and more satisfied overall with the hospital experience. In the same study, however, the nonreactors responded less well both to analgesics and to placebos for pain relief, raising the question of whether the reactors simply had less severe pain. A later study (Muller 1965), done in a laboratory and thus perhaps not comparable to Lasagna's hospital data, held that reactors by psychological testing were more enthusiastic, outgoing, and verbal, and better adjusted, than nonreactors; this picture seems to conflict with Lasagna's at several points. Still another study (Gartner 1961) found no difference between reactors and nonreactors when the same psychological test instrument was used, but a separate personality inventory showed reactors to be more neurotic and extraverted. In sum, there are so many inconsistencies among these and many other studies that one may reasonably conclude that no single personality type characterizes placebo reactors (Kurland 1960; Shapiro 1968). There may be evidence, however, to suggest that patients who develop worsening of symptoms on placebo may be distinguishable by some personality measures from either positive reactors or nonreactors (Shapiro et al. 1973).

In more cases than not, an individual who responds to placebo in one set of circumstances will fail to respond in other circumstances, even in the course of the same study; these inconsistent reactors generally outnumber consistent reactors and consistent nonreactors combined (Lasagna et al. 1954; Beecher 1955). The only study to show a nearly 100 percent constancy of reaction or nonreaction, an investigation of headache, has never been replicated (Jellinek 1946).

A large number of other patient variables have shown either no correlation or contradictory correlation with the placebo response. These include age, sex, intelligence, findings on Rorschach and other psychological tests, and presence of neurosis or psychosis (Shapiro 1968).

One characteristic of patients that has been rather consistently correlated with placebo reactivity is stress or anxiety. Even here there are questions, however. Beecher (1955) claimed that patients with more severe pain were more likely to get relief from placebos, and suggested that the psychic stress accompanying pain contributed to the placebo effect; but as already noted, Lasagna and his coworkers found the opposite correlation between pain severity and placebo response (Lasagna et al. 1954; Lasagna, Laties, and Dohan 1958). In treatment of anxiety neurosis, Rickels and Downing (1967) found that patients with less pretreatment anxiety responded better to placebos.

Other patient factors correlated with placebo reactivity are harder to measure. These include positive expectation, faith in the physician, motivation, and the need for emotional catharsis or for psychological defense mechanisms (such as the ritual of taking medicine as a means for reducing anxiety). A study of patients with paranoid symptoms found that those who exhibited readiness to enter into personal relationships with the therapists were good placebo reactors, whereas those holding back from such relationships were not (Freedman et al. 1967).

Expectations are commonly cited as an important factor in producing the placebo response. In a study of placebo to improve short-term memory in elderly patients, patients' expectations were highly correlated with subjective improvement, and less well with objective improvement (Nash and Zimring 1969). One detailed attempt to study the role of expectation occurred in a study of how biofeedback could increase the frequency of alpha rhythm (relaxation) on the subjects' encephalograms (Stoebel and Glueck 1973). The investigators designed an index to measure the combination of actual learning of alpha control and placebo effect. Using this index, they showed that patients did best in the long run when expectations and active learning were kept in relative balance. For instance, subjects with very high initial expectations tended to be discouraged by the actual results first obtained and thus performed less well on subsequent training. This index, however, is rather speculative in nature and perhaps ought to be viewed as a predictor of long-term outcome rather than as a measure of placebo effect.[5] Also, these investigators seem not to have distinguished carefully enough between expectation and motivation; each may well contribute to a positive outcome, but through different mechanisms (Rosenthal and Frank 1956). But if accepted, the results of this study suggest that either too high or too low expectations hamper placebo response.

Clearly, factors such as expectations and motivation are not patient variables, strictly speaking, but could be expected to depend at least in part on the physician, the situation in which the placebo is administered, and other external factors:

> [Expectations] vary widely among patients, depending on such factors as the patient's previous experiences with physicians and medications, his

> personal knowledge of the physician, the reputation of his physician in the community, the community belief in the recent achievements of medical science, various relevant properties of the institution or the setting in which the physician operates, and the physician's personality and behavior and his own expectancies as to what he can accomplish (Whitehorn 1958, p. 662).

While investigators for the most part have been reluctant to switch their attention from the placebo and the patient to the entire placebo context, accumulating data have forced this change in focus (Wolf 1959, Shapiro 1968).[6]

In the absence of objective data on the contribution of the physician to the placebo effect, a good many generalizations are based on other types of research, such as studies of experimenter bias in research and of the influence of therapists' behaviors and attitudes on outcome in psychotherapy (Shapiro 1968). A classic study of experimenter bias had the experimenters being told that their rats had been especially bred either for brightness or for dullness, although all rats were in fact from the same genetic strain. The experimenters then performed learning experiments on their rats and obtained data that conformed to whatever their expectations of the rats' behavior had been (Rosenthal 1963). If scientists can somehow communicate their own expectations and attitudes to rats, it seems reasonable to assume that physicians can unknowingly communicate expectations and attitudes to patients, altering the patients' therapeutic outcomes as a result.

One study that did document the physician's attitude as a factor in treatment compared relief of anxiety by two sedatives and by placebo. When the drugs were administered by one doctor, who anticipated that there would be no difference among the two active drugs and who was viewed by patients as more neutral and matter-of-fact in manner, there were no differences in relief among the three agents. When administered by a second doctor, who anticipated greater efficacy of the active drugs and whom the patients viewed as more optimistic and supportive, the two sedatives showed superiority to the placebo. In addition, patients showed greater overall relief of symptoms when treated by the second doctor. It might be inferred that the two physicians had in fact found a way to guess correctly which pills were sedatives and which were placebo and that the double-blind experimental design had broken down; but this was checked for and found not to be the case (Uhlenhuth et al. 1959).

1.5 THEORIES OF PLACEBO MECHANISMS
All medical authorities speculating on how placebos may exert their influence agree on one point—that a placebo "cannot possibly act" through a pharmocologic or physiologic route (Beecher 1955). Implicit or explicit in most investigators' definitions is that if a substance now held to be placebo, such as lactose, turns out to have a biochemical effect, this datum will prompt the reclassification of the substance as an active drug and will not be accepted as empirical evidence to explain the placebo effect. Also implicit in most views is the assumption that as we learn more about the specific physiologic and psychologic mechanisms of drugs and other treatments, the realm of effects now attributed to placebos will shrink (Shapiro 1964)—that is, that to call something a *placebo effect* is now as much an admission of ignorance as a potential explanation.

Elucidating the intermediary mechanisms by which placebos as well as other psychological interventions produce their bodily effects is not necessarily the same as proposing theories of placebo efficacy. A widely heralded study (Levine, Gordon, and Fields 1978) demonstrated that placebo administration increased circulating levels of endorphins (endogenous pain-relieving, opiatelike chemicals) in placebo responders but not in nonresponders; furthermore, naloxone, a proved endorphin antagonist, reversed the placebo-induced pain reduction. The medical press trumpeted this study as a major breakthrough in understanding how placebos work generally (a claim notably absent from the authors' paper), and suggested that placebos had somehow become more respectable now that a physiologic basis for their actions had been described. Of course, as already noted, pain relief is only one among innumerable symptomatic changes attributable to placebos; one could hardly expect to explain how placebos can lower the blood-sugar level in diabetics, for example, on the basis of endorphin secretion. The work of Levine et al. does suggest that placebos act to reduce pain through some psychological mechanism, since endorphins originate in the brain and are responsive to emotional changes.

Byerly (1976)[7] has classified possible placebo theories as mentalistic, conditioning, or mixed. Mentalistic theories presumably are those that make reference to the patient's subjective states of awareness, whereas conditioning theories are behavioristic accounts that make reference only to outwardly observable behavior.

The most commonly encountered mentalistic theories are those referring to patient expectation (e.g., Rosenthal and Frank 1956; Nash and Zimring 1969); such theories are also sometimes referred to as self-fulfilling prophecy (Beecher 1955) or response-bias theory (Morris and O'Neal 1974). By all these theories the patient's expectation of symptom change is held to be causally connected to the change that occurs. Since the central nervous system, the autonomic nervous system, and the endocrine system all exhibit predictable changes in response to the person's emotional state, these are frequently suggested as intervening psychophysiologic mechanisms (Wolf 1959).

Theories that are almost purely mentalistic hold that the placebo effect works solely through alteration of the patient's subjective reaction to illness. In pain relief, the placebo is said to act strictly to relieve anxiety, and this relief in turn produces relief of pain (Evans 1974); or pain itself is said to consist of a sensory component and a subjective-processing component, with the placebo affecting the latter and not the former (Beecher

1955).[8] But these theories ignore both the ability of placebos to relieve many other symptoms besides pain and the documented impact of placebos on objectively observable bodily function; such data seem to render any purely mentalistic theory untenable and to require some sort of psychophysiologic view.

Another form of mentalistic theory, arising from the Freudian tradition, is based on the concept of transference (Forrer 1964). This concept is defined in psychoanalysis as the unconscious projection of feelings, attitudes, and wishes properly displayed toward a significant figure in early development (usually the parent) onto another person in the individual's current life (the doctor or therapist) (Freedman, Kaplan, and Sadock 1972, p. 798). A satisfactory doctor-patient relationship invites the patient unconsciously to trust in the doctor, to submit to his wishes, and to expect him to "make it better" in a way similar to the parent-child relationship (Shapiro 1968). Transference may be seen as an adjunct to expectation theory, if positive transference encourages optimistic expectations, or it may be seen as an independent mechanism, acting, for example, through an unconscious release of psychic tensions.

Some theorists have attempted to reduce placebo responsiveness to suggestibility, which may be defined as a state of compliant responsiveness to ideas or influences (Freedman, Kaplan, and Sadock 1972, p. 795); susceptibility to hypnosis is a commonly cited example of suggestibility. But Shapiro notes that patients experiencing hysterical conversion reactions (psychic symptoms), patients commonly considered to be extremely suggestible in the way most psychologists use the term, are very poor placebo reactors; he feels that this casts doubt on the suggestibility theory (Shapiro 1968). But other investigators question whether the conversion hysteric is a true case of suggestibility as defined above (Kurland 1960). In one study (Steinbrook, Jones, and Ainslie 1965), the more suggestible patients showed significantly greater placebo reactivity in the first week of therapy, but later show less reactivity than other patients. The authors proposed that the more suggestible patients might overrespond to placebo at first, producing an apparent, relative worsening of symptoms later on; at any rate, suggestibility alone could not account for the extent and duration of the placebo effect.

In contrast to these various mentalistic theories, conditioning theory takes a stimulus-response form which makes no reference to the internal, mental states of the individual. Past instances of active therapy in medical settings are seen as the stimulus, and relief of symptoms is the original, unconditioned response. As conditioning occurs, the medical setting itself becomes a sufficient stimulus and the therapeutic response becomes conditioned, so that it occurs even without active treatment (just as, with Pavlov's dogs, a bell alone finally produces salivation) (Gliedman, Gantt, and Teitelbaum 1957).

Difficulty in choosing among competing theories is illustrated by Bourne (1971), who argues that transference and conditioning suffice equally well to explain some of the commonly observed placebo phenomena:

FINDING: Placebo response is maximized by anxiety.

TRANSFERENCE ACCOUNT: Anxiety produces a "set" for transference, by encouraging regressive behaviors harking back to an earlier stage of psychic development.

CONDITIONING ACCOUNT: Stress causes the organism to fall back on conditioned responses instead of trying new adaptive behaviors.

FINDING: Placebos often work best in diseases characterized by quiescent periods broken by periodic flare-ups.

TRANSFERENCE ACCOUNT: Recognition of experiences undergone in the past, such as a disease flare-up occurring as part of a recognized pattern, increases transference potential.

CONDITIONING ACCOUNT: Repetition of the stimulus is essential for conditioning to occur.

FINDING: Placebos work best on symptoms under central nervous system, autonomic, or hormonal control.

TRANSFERENCE ACCOUNT: Such symptoms are most susceptible to changes resulting from increase or decrease in psychic tension.

CONDITIONING ACCOUNT: Such bodily changes are most accessible to conditioning, being physiologically most closely connected with sensory inputs.

An additional mechanism proposed to explain the placebo effect is attribution theory. This is not a conditioning theory but does not seem to be clearly mentalistic either. Rather, it holds that placebo reactors are simply highly sensitive to subtle changes in their internal states. If a symptom lessens very slightly in severity following placebo administration, the individual detects this and attributes the change to the placebo. One study of placebo response (Nash and Zimring 1969) attempted to measure this internal sensitivity or "openness"; they found it not to be correlated with placebo reactivity, although patients' expectations were.

Another study (Morris and O'Neal 1974) set out to test alternative theories by giving placebos labeled with either familiar or unfamiliar drug names. According to conditioning theory, they reasoned, familiarity should enhance the placebo effect by providing a stronger conditioned stimulus. According to attribution theory, however, unfamiliarity might be expected to enhance the placebo effect, as the patient would be familiar with and sensitive to the pharmacologic effects of drugs that he had previously taken. According to expectation theory the physician's suggestion and attitude should be the controlling variable, with familiarity playing only a minor role. These investigators found no correlation of placebo response with familiarity or unfamiliarity, concluding that their results were most consistent with expectation theory.

Finally, Byerly (1976) has suggested the possibility of other theories which avoid the rigid distinction between mental and bodily phenomena; as an example he cites a view of the symbolic reality of medicine which treats disease as inherently a cultural construct (Kleinman 1973). Earlier placebo writers mention the symbolic aspects without making clear whether they are construing symbolic import in strictly mentalistic terms, or whether they hold, with Kleinman, that symbolic significance influences bodily health and disease:

> The physician is a vastly more important institution than the drug store. The reasons for this are deeply rooted in the mainsprings of human behavior, for man in distress wants action—rational action if possible, of course, but irrational action, if necessary, rather than none at all.... The pill the patient swallows, no matter what its nature, acquires potency as a symbol of faith, wisdom, and support (Findley 1953, pp. 1822–23).
>
> The physician's ability to relieve the emotional, reactive aspects of a patient's illness through symbolic operations is therefore an important aspect of his healing function.... Hence the prescription, pill or injection symbolizes the physician's healing function. The prescribing of a pharmacologically inert substance may thus, through its symbolic significance, produce favorable effects (Whitehorn 1958, p. 662).

The clearest theoretical statement of a symbolic-cultural basis for the placebo effect is given by Adler and Hammett (1973) in what I shall be calling the *meaning model* of the placebo effect. Adler and Hammett identify two invariant features of healing practices in all cultures: (1) a shared cognitive system which explains illness in terms (whether of natural phenomena or of supernatural occurrences) readily understandable to those sharing the background of cultural beliefs (*system formation*); and (2) a relationship with a socially sanctioned healer occupying a role of parental power and influence, which in turn stimulates caring responses from family and community (*group formation*):

> It is suggested here that these two factors—group formation and system formation—are as essential to psychic functioning as nourishment is to physical functioning, are the basic factors composing what is subjectively experienced as a feeling of "meaning," are invariably used in all successful interpersonal therapies, and are the necessary and sufficient components of the placebo effect (p. 597).

The data now available are insufficient to exclude with certainty any of the theories discussed above.[9] More research needs to be done, especially research like the Morris and O'Neal (1974) study cited above which sets out to compare different theories. Future strategy may stress research into the healing situation as a whole and into its symbolic and cultural aspects, but to a great extent interpretation of any future data will depend on defining more precisely what is meant by placebo effect and which phenomena are or are not applicable to its study. In addition, a study of what some of the placebo theories imply about the nature of the mind-body relation may provide additional grounds for accepting or dismissing them.[10]

TWO

A Definition of the Placebo Effect

The definitions of *placebo* by medical authors reviewed in chapter 1 lack rigorous analysis and are, indeed, mutually contradictory in some ways. Formulated primarily to introduce and organize various medical findings, they cannot be expected to bear much philosophical weight. My purpose is to formulate, in their stead, a definition of *placebo effect* that can serve as a basis for further philosophical investigation.

2.1 THE PLACEBO EFFECT AS MEDICAL ANOMALY

Kuhn's (1970) reconstruction of the history of science contains concepts that can be usefully applied to the placebo effect. Scientists conducting research rely heavily not only on the explicitly stated laws and theories of their science, but also on a set of assumptions and explanatory presuppositions which remains implicit but which uniquely characterizes the science they are engaged in. These presuppositions create expectations about the world and suggest both what sorts of phenomena are most usefully studied and how observations or experiments are best carried out. The presuppositions are thus very useful in guiding scientific research and in steering scientists away from troublesome areas not accessible to the scientific tools at hand. But invariably data are collected which are at odds with this set of presuppositions and which are unexpected according to accepted laws and theories. Scientists first attempt to account for these findings by making slight modifications in the existing theories; but over time, more and more unexpected findings accumulate. At some point a few "revolutionary" scientists put forth totally new laws and theories based on a different set of presuppositions. If this new set of theories explains the previously unaccounted-for data, embraces the accumulated knowledge of the old science, and opens up new avenues for further research, scientists will eventually adopt it, and a scientific revolution will have occurred. Kuhn terms the set of basic presuppositions and assumptions a *paradigm*[1] and calls the unexpected findings that can lead to overturning paradigms, *anomalies*.

An example from physics may illustrate how paradigms and anomalies are related. The paradigm dominant in physics in 1895 led scientists to expect to find various sorts of rays, but not rays that could cause a plate to glow across the room from a cathode ray tube. Thus, when Roentgen noticed such a glow, he was observing a phenomenon which had previously been created in many other laboratories but never observed, because the theories and the presuppositions of physics did not tell anyone to look for it. (By contrast, a totally expected finding might be the discovery of a new element whose properties had already been predicted by the periodic table.) Roentgen's announcement of his discovery, therefore, stirred immediate controversy. At the very least, accepting his data would require that many accepted experiments be done over, since this new variable now had to be controlled. The clash with existing assumptions was so strong that some eminent physicists, such as Lord Kelvin, refused to believe Roentgen's data. About the same time, however, physics was accumulating other anomalies, including black-body radiation and the constancy of the speed of light; and so when the new paradigms of quantum mechanics and relativity appeared, which could account for these anomalies better than the old Newtonian paradigm, physics was ready to accept them (Kuhn 1970, pp. 57–61).

In medicine, underlying paradigms include theories and assumptions about the nature of disease and therapy and about laws and regularities in human pathophysiology. The present-day, Western medical paradigm emphasizes causal mechanisms affecting organs, tissues, cells, chemical factors, and physical phenomena. Theories relating psychological and sociological factors to disease and therapy are generally less well developed and held in lower esteem—as though one might feel that they will have to do until "real" explanations in physical-chemical terms become available through further research. Within such a paradigm, the fact that a chemically inert pill can change symptoms and organic bodily states constitutes a significant anomaly. As in the case of X-rays, accepting the placebo phenomenon entails rejecting a major body of previously accepted data, since until recently, most of what was known about therapeutics came from uncontrolled trials. A discovery such as the placebo effect is likely to arouse consternation among medical scientists, unlike the discovery, for instance, of a new antibiotic to treat tuberculosis; the dominant paradigm leads the scientist to expect the latter but not the former.

In the absence of an attractive alternative paradigm that can totally replace the existing medical paradigm, we see different attempts to deal with the placebo discovery. The serious physician today cannot deny the placebo data; but he can adopt an attitude toward it of exclusion, i.e., labeling the placebo effect so that it can be readily recognized and thus excluded from research. The early attempts to determine a placebo-reactor personality type so that such subjects could be excluded from clinical trials (§1.4) is an example of this approach; the scientist reasons that he might as well focus his attention on those phenomena which are most readily explainable by accepted theories and put any anomalies he finds "on the shelf." The suggestion that the placebo effect is an impurity which ought to be removed from psychotherapeutic modalities (Shapiro 1964) is another example of exclusionary thinking. This sort of thinking may influence and may implicitly operate in the definition one adopts for *placebo* and *placebo effect*.

By contrast, an inclusive approach would seek new laws or causal factors, to expand or modify the existing paradigm so as to bring the placebo effect within it. The fact that the dominant paradigm has grudgingly admitted phenomena such as psychosomatic disease might lead one to think that this expansion or modification need not be drastic and that the paradigm will emerge stronger for the change. Research studies which view the placebo effect as a phenomenon to be studied on its own grounds rather than as a variable to be controlled, exemplify the inclusionary approach.

X-rays are anomalous from the viewpoint of the Newtonian paradigm but not from the viewpoint of modern physics. Similarly, how one construes the phenomena we have been calling the placebo effect depends on the paradigm of reference. Consider an African native village with two witch doctors who use essentially identical healing rituals; an anthropologist discovers that one is viewed by the villagers as more highly expert at his craft and that that one achieves a significantly higher cure rate than the other. The anthropologist might conclude that (1) all healing accomplished by either witch doctor is due either to the placebo effect or to the normal vicissitudes of disease, and (2) the greater healing rate of the one is due to a differential placebo effect, produced by greater expectations on the part of the patients. But this is to view the matter from the Western paradigm, which holds treatment not explainable in our accepted theoretical terms as biomedically inefficacious. The disease paradigm operating in that village, however, may hold that a witch doctor's cure always works unless the patient fails to follow directions exactly or thinks impure thoughts while involved in the ritual; all treatment failures may be explained in these terms. The villagers might then postulate that the more respected witch doctor is better able to banish impure thoughts and to command compliance from his patients. Not only does this paradigm explain the phenomenon that we would attribute to the placebo effect in totally different terms, but it seems to leave no room within its explanatory model for anything like the placebo effect at all.

Thus when Shapiro claims that the history of medicine before the present century is the history of the placebo effect (1968, p. 597), he is saying that therapies then in use are deemed worthless by modern medical science and that patients nevertheless got better at a rate not attributable entirely to the natural recuperative powers of the body.[2] But this is again to apply our present paradigm uncritically; a serious medical historian would seek rather to determine what paradigms dominated the thinking of those earlier physicians. (I will suggest later that the use of the term *placebo effect* in Shapiro's statement can be understood only in a derivative or metaphorical sense.)

Since the placebo effect is already a rather slippery concept, one might want to begin the task of defining it by accepting at least one firm reference point; for my discussion, this will be our currently accepted medical paradigm.

2.2 BOUNDARIES OF THE PLACEBO EFFECT

The term *placebo effect* can be construed very narrowly to refer to only a few sorts of phenomena, or very broadly to include much of medical practice and many nonmedical occurrences as well. There are some "core" uses of the term that almost all medical scientists would agree to; and there are uses of the term near the boundaries of its applicability that might engender considerable debate. To get clear on these boundary conditions and to provide a basis for a formal definition of placebo effect, consider a series of illustrative examples showing what is at stake if we draw the boundary lines at various points.

> CASE 1. A patient suffers from pain due to periodic flareups of rheumatoid arthritis. During one such episode the physician administers sugar capsules, telling the pa-

tient that this is a new analgesic drug. The patient subsequently reports dramatic relief.

Case 1 seems to be a straightforward, uncomplicated instance of the "core" sense of the term *placebo effect*.[3] None of the medical authors cited in chapter 1 would hesitate to apply the term in such a case.

> CASE 2. *A* and *B* both contract a cold at the same time in similar circumstances. *A* is administered a sugar pill and told that it is a potent cold remedy; *B* gets no treatment. Both *A* and *B* recover from their symptoms at the same rate, with the same level of discomfort until their colds subside.

Would one want to say in case 2 that *A* experienced a placebo effect? By current medical thinking, the recovery of both *A* and *B* can be explained on the basis of the self-limiting aspects of viral infections, immune defense mechanisms, restoration of homeostatic processes, and so forth. There are thus good grounds to regard the taking of the sugar pill as irrelevant to *A*'s course—all things being equal, he would have gotten better in an identical fashion without the pill. It would sound paradoxical to attribute an effect to an intervention which played no role in the outcome; and on this analysis we would not regard case 2 as an example of the placebo effect. We would rather say that both *A* and *B* got better as a result of the body's natural restorative processes.

Suppose on the other hand that one wanted to argue for a possible role for the placebo effect in case 2. One would then be postulating the presence of a placebo effect that would not be discoverable in terms of observable outcome. I will assume that one purpose of defining the placebo effect is to stimulate and guide empirical research into its workings and that adequate understanding of it will involve empirical issues as well as conceptual ones. Given that purpose, there is nothing to be gained, and some measure of clarity to be lost, in postulating a placebo effect in case 2.

> CASE 3. A large number of individuals are suffering from

a wide variety of diseases. Half of these individuals are fed an especially nutritious diet, whereas the other half are fed a nutritionally inadequate diet. A larger percentage of the first group recover, compared to the second group, although a number of individuals in the first do grow worse despite the diet.[4]

The effect of diet on disease resistance has some features in common with the placebo effect. The same basic diet will be effective for a large number of diseases. There is a measureable positive response to diet therapy, but it generally falls well below 100 percent (except in cases of specific nutritional deficiencies). And the diet presumably does nothing directly to alter the basic causative mechanism of the disease (microbes, cellular malignancy, or whatever).

But, as with the so-called natural restorative powers, we can explain the results of nutritional therapy by pathophysiologic theories that appear to be independent of the placebo effect. Postulating a placebo effect in case 3 as it stands would appear to multiply explanations needlessly (assuming that the improvement of the first group is not over and above the amount that can be explained on the basis of the theories alluded to). The features that nutrition and the placebo effect have in common suggest what medical authors have in mind when they refer to *nonspecific therapies*. Exercise and modalities which enhance the efficacy of the body's immune system might be cited as other examples of nonspecific therapy (which itself stands in need of formal definition). Thus the placebo effect is one type of nonspecific therapy but is not coextensive with that class.

CASE 4. Imipramine is the drug of choice for treating certain types of depression. Both Dr. *A* and Dr. *B* use this drug, with the same dosage schedules, on large numbers of depressed patients. Dr. *A* is surly to his patients, whereas Dr. *B* is encouraging and supportive. In three weeks' time 75 percent of Dr. *A*'s patients—but 90 percent of Dr. *B*'s—improved significantly.

Imipramine is certainly not an inert substance; it is both active and specific for the condition being treated. But to explain the different results (again assuming the patient populations otherwise equal), we are inclined to view the total therapy as consisting of the drug plus the emotional-psychological features of the doctor's interaction with the patient. Like many investigators, we have been forced by the data to turn our attention away from the drug itself and to look instead at the total context (§1.4), and on this basis we might attribute Dr. *B*'s increased success rate to a placebo effect. If we do, we are using *placebo effect* to designate the results of one component of the therapy—a component which in the actual setting might be so intermingled with other features of the doctor-patient exchange as to be practically indistinguishable.[5] This is different from the simple sugar-pill case, but on balance it seems a reasonable extension of the term. Some medical authors (Houston 1938; Wolf 1959; Shapiro 1968) define *placebo effect* to allow for this use, whereas others (Pepper 1945) do not.

> CASE 5. A person who never goes to doctors decides to improve his health by undertaking an exercise program. He develops strength and endurance, as well as a more general sense of fitness and well-being.[6]

In case 4 we explained the total result in terms of both pathophysiological and psychological features, and we attributed the latter component to the placebo effect. The increase in strength and endurance in case 5 can be explained as specific outcomes of exercise. On the face of it the psychological sense of well-being one gets in addition does not seem dissimilar from the added boost that a supportive doctor-patient relationship can give to an active medication. Is there any reason not to attribute this result to a placebo effect of the exercise?

To argue for such a reason I must introduce the notion of the *healing context*. This is derived from the concept of the *sick role* first intoduced by medical sociologists, which has proved very useful in cross-cultural studies of response to illness.[7]

One feature of the sick role is that the sick person must submit to the authority of the socially designated healer for the purposes of attempting a cure. While the healer may be a medical doctor, a herbalist, a shaman, or whatever, such socially designated healing roles exist in virtually every culture that has been studied. Furthermore, it is usual, if not universal, for a particular setting—hospital, cave, temple, etc.—to be identified with the healing activity and for certain ritual behaviors (often including behaviors not tolerated by that culture anywhere else) to become associated with that setting and with the purpose of healing. This combination of the designated healer, designated setting, and designated rituals I refer to as the healing context. It refers to something present in all cultures, without specifying the precise healing practices of any particular culture or the beliefs of any particular medical paradigm. As a rule, of course, the psychological reaction of the patient in the healing context can be elicited only if the culture-bound features of the healing context are those of the patient's own culture.[8] Considering the universality of patterns of social response to sickness, we can reasonably assume, I think, that there are important similarities, say, between the native's psychological reaction to being in the shaman's temple and the Western individual's reaction to hospitalization.

The question posed by case 5, then, is whether we wish to impose as a boundary condition on the term *placebo effect* that it apply only to events occurring within a healing context. Even this condition may be too weak, as case 6 illustrates.

> CASE 6. A patient in acceptable physical condition who is scheduled to undergo open heart surgery becomes very depressed and insists, despite support and reassurance from the medical staff, that he is sure that he is going to die during surgery. The operation is begun and all is going well until, for no apparent reason, there is a sudden drop in blood pressure. All attempts to correct this fail and the patient dies.

The ability of persons to "think" themselves into otherwise

unexplainable deaths is well documented (Frank 1974, pp. 50–55; Engel 1978).[9] If we follow Shapiro's reasonable convention of identifying placebo effects as potentially either positive or negative, could we attribute the death in case 6 to a negative placebo effect? Unlike the situation in case 5, the events in question occur within the healing context. But the psychological effect, depression, is neither an intended result of the therapeutic intervention nor a concomitant thereof (as in case 4); indeed the doctors in case 6 try deliberately, although unsuccessfully, to counteract the depression.

Cases 5 and 6 suggest a conceptual "slippery-slope" problem with the boundaries of placebo effect. There are an almost endless number of instances where suggestion, or autosuggestion, or other psychological states influence bodily processes or perceptions of bodily processes (Frank 1974; Kiritz and Moos 1974). The psychophysiological mechanisms by which these occur require empirical elucidation. Although it would be surprising if the mechanisms by which a sugar pill can ameliorate symptoms turned out to be totally different from the mechanisms involved in these other instances, the precise degree of similarity or dissimilarity needs to be investigated; it does not seem to be a matter to be decided by definitional fiat.

I have suggested already that the task of defining *placebo effect* can be viewed as a preparatory step toward this needed research. In what ways, then, can the choice of definition either help or hinder research? It would help if the definition called attention to similarities that investigators had not already discerned between the defined phenomenon and an already known class of events. But the placebo literature shows no reluctance to view the placebo effect in light of what is known about other psychophysiologic correlations—we have already reviewed attempts to apply such standard psychophysiologic theories as conditioning and transference to the placebo problem (§1.5).

Alternatively, a definition would hinder research if it were too inclusive, tempting the investigator to pass over important differences among classes of phenomena. For instance, so long as respiratory diseases caused by bacteria, mycoplasma, and viruses were all lumped together as pneumonia, investigation of the role of penicillin in treatment was bound to be impeded. We saw earlier (§1.3) how much remains to be learned about the psychophysiologic phenomena that occur within and as part of the healing context. A reasonable research strategy, I assume, would be to shed light on these instances before trying to generalize the findings to other aspects of human existence. If one accepts this empirical bias and strategic assumption, it makes good sense to exclude the phenomena described in cases 5 and 6 from the definition of *placebo effect*.[10]

> CASE 7. *A* is a Christian Scientist and, despite being severely ill with rheumatoid arthritis, refuses to take any sort of drug or other medical therapy. *B,* who is concerned about *A*'s welfare, knows of studies showing that arthritic patients improve when given a placebo such as lactose. *B* obtains a supply of pink lactose tablets, but, knowing *A*'s aversion to medication, contrives to slip the tablets into *A*'s coffee without *A*'s knowledge.[11]

Case 7 points out another feature of the healing context as it relates to the placebo effect. It makes sense to say that *B* has slipped a sugar pill into *A*'s coffee, but does it make sense to say that *B* has slipped a placebo into *A*'s coffee? The latter seems to involve a conceptual absurdity, regardless of whether *A*'s condition changes or not.[12] The lesson of case 7 is that it is not enough for the subject to be in a healing context in order to warrant use of the term *placebo effect;* the subject must *believe* that he is in a healing context. Generalizing from numerous studies, one may conclude that the subject need not believe the treatment being given is efficacious,[13] but only that it is treatment, a deliberate intervention given in response to his illness with beneficial intent.

Suppose that we inform *B* of his conceptual error, and he now must decide what to do with his large supply of pink tablets. If he uses them in his own coffee, as a sweetener, we would not say he is using placebos on himself. We have already noted the empirical findings that have led placebo investigators to focus on the context of placebo use, not on the dummy treatment itself; our analysis of case 7 adds to this empirical observation the stronger conceptual point that the meaning of *placebo effect* is context-dependent in the way that we have noted.

If belief in the healing context is a necessary condition, is it also sufficient? Imagine an elaborate sham in which an individual is made to believe, wrongly, that he is in a clinic receiving treatment from a doctor, when in fact he is getting dummy pills and shots from actors on a movie set. If the victim of this subterfuge experiences a relief of symptoms attributable to his experience, we can say without contradiction that a placebo effect has occurred. We might even want to go so far as to say that the belief itself is sufficient to make the movie set a healing context *for that individual* in his present belief state, just as a witch doctor's thatched hut may be a healing context for an African native but not for a Wall Street stockbroker. For our present purposes, however, we need not debate this point. From a practical standpoint, examples such as the movie-set sham do not pose any significant problem for defining *placebo effect,* however they may help to isolate the key features of healing contexts.

Before turning, finally, to the matter of formal definitions, it is important to emphasize the difference between the boundary conditions indicated by cases 5 and 6 and case 7. The boundary condition of the former two cases—requiring the healing context as a necessary condition—is a stipulative device suggested because of its probable utility for research. But the boundary condition of the latter—requiring belief in the existence of a healing context—is conceptual and points out an essential feature of the word *placebo.*[14]

2.3 FORMAL DEFINITION OF *Placebo Effect*

Using the material of the preceding section, let us first evaluate critically the formal and informal definitions offered by medical authors and then make suitable changes. Four major definitions, already cited in §1.1, may be summarized as follows:

1. Pepper (1945): The placebo effect is a therapeutic effect produced by a biomedically inert substance.
2. Wolf (1959): The placebo effect is a therapeutic effect or side effect attributable to a treatment, but not to its pharmacologic properties.
3. Shapiro (1968, p. 599): The placebo effect is the nonspecific effect of a therapy that may or may not have a specific effect in addition.
4. Modell (1955, p. 55): The placebo effect is what all treatments have in common.

These definitions are listed in order of increasing breadth and the increasing range of phenomena that fall under them. For instance, Pepper's definition implies that if a specific pharmacologic effect is present, the placebo effect *cannot* be present; Wolf's and Shapiro's, that if a specific pharmacologic effect is present, the placebo effect *may* also be present; and Modell's, that if a specific pharmacologic effect is present, the placebo effect *must* be present.

On grounds already discussed we can eliminate the narrowest and the broadest of these four proposals. Pepper's approach is ruled out by our willingness to look at different components of a total therapeutic encounter and to ascribe a placebo effect to a nonspecific component which might accompany administration of an active treatment. Modell's all-inclusive statement is refuted by an example mirroring case 7. In Wilkie Collins's novel *The Moonstone* (1868), a physician, angered by statements from the hero on the total worthlessness of medicine, secretly places some laudanum in the hero's coffee; and the hero, who had previously been troubled by insomnia, sleeps unusually soundly that night. This is a clear case of pharmacologic potency without any accompanying placebo effect.[15]

The remaining proposals are substantially similar and are roughly consistent with our previous discussions. But they make uncritical use of the terms *therapy* and *nonspecific*, which seem to require some elucidation. I begin by offering a definition of *therapy:*

> T is a therapy for condition C if and only if it is believed that administration of T to a person with C increases the empirical probability that C will be cured, relieved, or ameliorated, as compared to the probability that this will occur without T.

This definition is intended to be as general as possible, embracing drugs, surgery, physical therapy, psychotherapy, and so on, even though it does not include measures aimed solely at prevention of disease. "Administration" should be interpreted to include acts of omission (such as salt restriction) and therapy administered by the person himself, but it is also intended to restrict *therapy* to acts of deliberate intervention or human agency. The definition does not explicitly require that condition C be a disease or a symptom of disease; this interesting issue is not pertinent to the matter at hand.

The phrase "it is believed that" is included to allow one to speak of ineffective therapies; if this were omitted, the definitions for *therapy* and *effective therapy* would be the same, contrary to general usage.[16] The definition also indicates implicitly when one is justified in believing that T will relieve C, by including the reference to empirical probability: either a randomized controlled study must show that T is more likely than no treatment to relieve C, or other theories of pathophysiology, themselves supported by empirical data, must predict T's efficacy using known causal mechanisms for C. Anecdotal evidence and personal experience justify the belief only in a derivative sense; one must be willing to assume that a future controlled trial, if carried out, would confirm this evidence. Therefore, this definition of *therapy* is dependent upon our present medical paradigm, which holds up the standard of the randomized, controlled trial over any other form of investigation. Following the definition, we might say that physicians of other historical periods, or in other cultures, used therapies; but by our present paradigm we would not be willing to say they were justified in considering these measures to be therapies. Note that these physicians could be considered justified by reference to the paradigm under which they were operating; the problem of cross-paradigm criticism and justification is a general problem in history and philosophy of science and is not peculiar to this definition or to the placebo problem.

By contrast, we might envision a culture which related the cause of all disease to transgressions against basic social mores and for whom therapy was seen in terms of atonement or expiation. This disease-therapy paradigm could be internally consistent and could promote social cohesiveness value as well, even to the extent that it might be irrelevant whether a particular therapy ever did any good for the individual patient in an empirically verifiable way. This culture might offer a definition of *therapy* which would be radically different from ours, but which in its own way would be equally paradigm-dependent.[17]

In general one is not justified in making empirical probability statements until one has observed a large number of instances. Thus, the acceptability criterion implied by the definition of *therapy* would prevent one from considering an intervention to be a therapy based on the observation of only one patient. Such a restriction is consistent with the present unwillingness in medicine to accept anecdotal evidence. If, then, we are later to define *placebo effect* in terms of a sort of therapy, it follows that to ascribe the placebo effect to one patient is implicitly to formulate a hypothesis about how a class of similar patients would behave in like circumstances. For example, to suggest that a depressed patient got better not only because of his imipramine but also because of the placebo effect of his positive relationship with his psychiatrist is to postulate a situation like that in case 4 in §2.2 above.

What might be meant by the next problematic term, *nonspecific therapy?* Consider different inferences that could be attached to the statement, "Digitalis is a specific therapy for congestive heart failure."

1. Digitalis is known to correct the direct cause of congestive heart failure (by strengthening the contractions of myocardial fibers).
2. Digitalis is the preferred therapy for congestive heart failure. That is, there is no alternative therapy that offers a better risk-benefit ratio, taking both therapeutic efficacy and potential toxic effects into account.
3. Digitalis is a therapy for only a small number of conditions, out of all those encountered in medicine. Therapies such as bed rest and gradual exercise are also efficacious in heart failure, as they are in many other conditions, but the effects of digitalis in heart failure are more prompt and more certain.

Whereas the phrase *specific therapy* is used in medical discourse most frequently in the first or the second sense above, the third sense makes clearest the contrast between specific and general therapy. Case 3 in §2.2 suggests that the placebo effect is a type of general therapy, along with diet, exercise, and so on. It is therefore reasonable to consider nonspecific therapy, when used in defining *placebo effect,* as being equivalent to general therapy in this sense. This third sense of *specific* is looser than the first and second, but seems to be what is required to make sense of *placebo effect;* thus we need not worry about providing a formal definition of *specific* to suit the stronger usages.

The following definition summarizes *specific* in the appropriate sense for our placebo definition:

T is a specific therapy for condition C if and only if:

1. T is a therapy for C,
2. there is a class A of conditions such that C is a subclass of A and that for all members of A, T is a therapy,

3. there is a class B of conditions such that for all members of B, T is not a therapy; and class B is much larger than class A.

For example, consider how the definition applies to penicillin used for pneumococcal pneumonia. Penicillin is a therapy for this disease, since it increases the empirical probability of recovery. Pneumococcal pneumonia is one of a class of diseases (infectious diseases caused by penicillin-sensitive organisms) for all of which penicillin is a therapy; but there is a much larger class of diseases (noninfectious diseases and infectious diseases caused by penicillin-resistant organisms) for which penicillin is not a therapy.

Recalling our discussion of digitalis, why did we not add as a fourth condition that T acts more promptly and more reliably for C than other therapies? To some extent the way we have defined *therapy* makes it redundant to talk about an efficacious therapy, since an intervention which is not likely to improve the condition is simply not a therapy. Furthermore, our goal is to contrast *specific therapy* with *general therapy*, so whether more efficacious alternative therapies exist is not important in this loose sense of *specific*.

We can now combine the foregoing elements into a definition of the placebo effect:

A placebo effect occurs for person X if and only if:

1. X has condition C,
2. X believes that he is within a healing context,
3. X is administered intervention I as part of that context, where I is either the total active intervention or some component of that intervention,
4. C is changed,
5. the change in C is attributable to I, but not to any specific therapeutic effect of I or to any known pharmacologic or physiologic property of I.

The mention of belief in the healing context and the possibility that I may be only one component of the total healing intervention reflect the boundary conditions discussed in §2.2.[18]

The definition, like Wolf's and Shapiro's, allows for both positive and negative changes in C. "Not attributable to any pharmacologic or physiologic property of I" excludes changes due to diet or other nonspecific therapies. To whatever extent psychotherapy can be shown empirically to be efficacious, it is also a specific therapy and so is excluded even though it has no "pharmacologic or physiologic" effect. The word "attributable" may be interpreted in light of our discussion of *therapy* and the acceptability criteria implicit in the current medical paradigm; it also refers to the present state of medical knowledge and leaves open the possibility that newly discovered properties of I may cause us to change our view that C was modified by the placebo effect.[19] It is even conceivable, from the form of the definition, that everything we now attribute to the placebo effect will someday be attributed to new laws of medicine, leaving *placebo effect* without reference. There are thus two very different epistemic elements in our definition—the belief state of the individual subject regarding the healing context and the belief state of medical science regarding what can be explained by existing laws and theories. The first is culture-dependent, the second paradigm-dependent.

It is admittedly unsatisfactory that *placebo effect* has been defined by exclusion, as something not attributable to other things. Why not an inclusive definition, such as one attributing the placebo effect directly to the psychological component of the healing intervention? Certainly in practice "not attributable to known pharmacologic or physiologic properties" could amount simply to "attributable to psychological properties"; but it could also mean attributable to currently unknown pharmacologic properties or to some completely different sort of property. This seems to be a matter best left for empirical research. Furthermore, if one framed an inclusive definition but failed to mention the property to which the placebo effect was to be attributed, one would merely have a definition of a nonspecific therapy and would be unable to distinguish the placebo effect and the effects of diet and exercise.

Significantly, I have offered a definition of *placebo effect* without having given a definition of *placebo*. This is in keeping with the trend we have already noted several times, of looking at the total context instead of at the inert medication. Thus, as case 4 shows, we can apply the term *placebo effect* to instances where no placebo is in evidence. In such cases one can label the purported causative component of the intervention the *placebo stimulus* to emphasize this distinction. We can then be satisfied with a more traditional, restricted definition of *placebo* proper:

A placebo is:

1. a form of medical therapy, or an intervention designed to simulate medical therapy, that at the time of use is believed not to be a specific therapy for the condition for which it is offered and that is used either for its psychological effect or to eliminate observer bias in an experimental setting,

2. (by extension from 1) a form of medical therapy now believed to be inefficacious, though believed efficacious at the time of use.

Clause 2 is added to make sense of a sentence such as, "Most of the medications used by physicians one hundred years ago were actually placebos." One of the epistemic elements from the definition of *placebo effect* reappears: the mention of the present belief state of medical science. Where a placebo is used for therapy, we can assume that the second epistemic element is present also, since to have a psychological effect the therapy must be believed to be such by the recipient (as case 7 illustrates). But this element of belief may be lacking in experimental settings where placebos also have an important role.

The definition given above satisfies the requirement that a definition of *placebo effect* aid and stimulate research. It asks the question: if the change in symptomatology is not attributable to known pharmacologic or physiologic properties of the intervention, to what is it attributable? At the same time, it avoids closing lines of research by a priori stipulations of what sorts of properties to consider. But beyond the empirical questions, I am concerned with the philosophical significance of the definition. One important line of investigation is suggested by the possibility that psychological mechanisms might produce bodily changes and that such changes depend on the belief state of the subject, a situation which would seem to have important consequences for theories of the mind-body relationship. A different line of investigation is the ethical question of the use of placebos as therapy, for which the formal definition given above also has significance.

THREE

Traditional Mind-Body Views and the Placebo Effect

Having reviewed the empirical data on the placebo effect and having formulated a definition of this phenomenon, we may now ask what implications our inquiry has for the mind-body relationship. By itself, the placebo effect raises interesting questions about philosophy of mind; but in addition, to the extent that *mens sana in corpore sano* is a goal of medical practice, these questions are central to any philosophy of medicine.

Devoting this and the next two chapters to mind-body issues may seem to be a disproportionate amount of attention, especially since so much of the present chapter merely lists possible theories only to reveal later their weaknesses and defects. But in fact, although all proposed mind-body theories have flaws, very few of them are outright nonsense; almost all theories capture some portion of the complex of intuitions that we hold about our bodies and our minds. In general, theories fail, not by failing to capture and illuminate the intuitions to which they are addressed, but rather by failing to take into account other, equally basic intuitions. Thus, reviewing many alternative theories will place us in a much better position to examine critically the theory we will, in the end, find most satisfactory, even if in the process we are led somewhat far afield from the placebo effect itself.

Despite the large amount of space being devoted to the

mind-body issues (as compared, say, to the ethical issues in chapter 6), it is necessary to skim rather lightly over many areas of possible controversy and to summarize in rough-and-ready fashion philosophical arguments that are very complex in their full development. Thus, the following discussion may suggest a wider philosophical agreement than is actually the case, as examination of the references cited will readily show.

3.1 A Reflective-Equilibrium Approach to Mind

If we accept the notion that the accumulated data about the placebo effect require some sort of explanation in terms of how the mind and the body are related and that this is a matter for philosophical analysis rather than for additional empirical research alone, we can approach the task of explanation in different ways. One is to seek out the view of the mind-body relationship which best explains the placebo effect as an isolated phenomenon, or which at least does not conflict with any of the known empirical findings. This view is not obliged to account for mind-body issues not directly raised by the placebo data (for instance, the question of whether minds can exist apart from bodies). It is consistent with the pragmatic, task-oriented way in which physicians and medical scientists have approached the mind-body problem, when they have approached it at all.[1] Thus, one finds in the medical literature proposals for "double-language theory" (Graham 1967), holist emergentism (Wolff 1962), and "methodological dualism" (Boss 1975). But as a rule, these accounts deal with medically related issues only at the expense of other features of a comprehensive philosophy of mind—whether minds can exist apart from bodies, whether we can know there are minds other than our own, and so on.[2] If a philosopher notes that a medical mind-body theory raises problems and conflicts in these other areas, it seems as if philosophy is simply raising impediments to medical research and progress. Small wonder in these circumstances that medical people come to regard the mind-body problem as "philosophically senseless and scientifically wasteful of time and effort" (Freedman, Kaplan, and Sadock 1972, p. 432).

An alternative approach is the *reflective equilibrium* strategy. Its task is to find the overarching theory that best makes what we know about the placebo effect cohere in a consistent and mutually illuminating way with other conceptual considerations regarding mind and body. Our particular concern with the placebo phenomenon should not make us forget that we have many basic considered judgments about mind and body. These might include, for example, our certainty that we need no grounds to ascribe a sensation such as pain to ourselves—we simple *are* in pain; we do not infer that we are—whereas we do need grounds to ascribe it to others. Nevertheless, we unhesitatingly treat another who is in pain as if he has the same sensation that we do when in pain ourselves. Although we want a mind-body theory that deals adequately with the placebo effect, we also require that our theory fit with basic considered judgments of the sort mentioned. We are willing to work from both ends, either giving up some fineness of grain regarding the placebo effect in exchange for better overall fit, or sacrificing some degree of fit for a theory which promises to highlight the placebo effect in a particularly illuminating way. If the search for this kind of broadly based theory fails, we may then wish to accept a narrow, medically oriented view. But since, in the course of searching for the best fit, we might find our considered judgments about other matters giving us new insight into the placebo effect, and vice versa, it would be a methodological mistake to settle for the narrow theory without making some attempt to search for a more comprehensive one first. Thus, we will consider mind-body theories both from the standpoint of the placebo effect and from the standpoint of our basic considered judgments. If the different theories give equally adequate, if equally vague, accounts of the placebo effect, then the basic considered judgments will play the larger role in ranking the different theories according to their philosophical plausibility.[3]

3.2 OVERVIEW OF ALTERNATIVE
MIND-BODY THEORIES

Almost all views of the mind-body relation assume there is a significant and basic difference between statements about sensations, volitons, thoughts, memories, etc., and statements about the structure and function of physical bodies.[4] Originally, Descartes characterized mind as thinking and unextended (i.e., neither occupying nor moving through physical space), and body as unthinking and extended. A human being was seen to consist of a mind plus a body.[5] Whereas mind was originally thought of as nonmaterial substance, difficulties with this concept have prompted use of the locution *mental events*. Mental events differ from physical events in that we have some sort of noninferential access to some of them (i.e., our own), so that as a rule we cannot be mistaken about them. Mental events, moreover, are not localizable in space in the precise way that physical events are.

Speaking of mental events in general clearly requires that we gloss over the distinctions between such very different things as smelling an unpleasant odor and thinking about a differential equation. While much of the discussion that follows is based on such a glossing over, it is nevertheless useful to distinguish two important types of mental events, sensations and intentional states. A rough way of making the distinction is to note that sensations include events such as hearing a bell, feeling a pain, seeing a bright color, and so on; they often correspond to something "out there" but not necessarily, as in cases of hallucinations and afterimages. Intentional states include believing that the Battle of Hastings was fought in 1066, thinking about the predicability of earthquakes, and fearing that you are going to hit me. These cannot be described completely without mentioning the object (often a proposition introduced by the word *that*), and the object need not be present or may not even exist—I can think about Moses or about unicorns. Also, as a rule, sensations are a more primitive sort of event; all sentient animals can have them, whereas only more complex organisms can have intentional states. As we might expect, some mind-body theories give good accounts of sensations but have difficulty with intentional states; other theories have the opposite characteristics. Behavioral analysis, in particular, seems better fitted for analyzing intentions than sensations.

If we recognize the mental and the physical as distinct and primitive types of events, we can deal with their relationship in two ways. We may choose a *monistic* theory that either recognizes the essential reality of only one of these types, or else tries to derive one type from the other, or both types from a third. Or we may select a *dualistic* theory which recognizes both types of events as equally basic and seeks to explain their relationship without slighting either.

One sort of monistic theory regards one type of event as totally dependent upon and arising secondarily from the other. *Idealism* attributes reality only to mental events and regards the physical world as totally dependent upon our mental images of it. A tree, for instance, would exist only as the object of someone's perception and would not exist at all if someone were not at that moment perceiving it. Idealistic theories are seldom proposed today. Much more popular is *materialism,* which holds that statements about mental events are really only statements about certain physical events occurring in the brain. For instance, our seeing a tree consists of photons of light striking the retina, exciting neurons to discharge, which in turn excite other neurons, and so on. When we have described all these physical events, we have said all there is to say about "seeing a tree"; there is nothing mental over and above these physical events. *Behaviorism,* which we can regard for our purposes as a form of materialism, seeks to reduce all statements about mental events to statements about the publicly observable behavior of organisms. The recent successes in neurophysiological research and in operant-conditioning psychology have made materialism and behaviorism, respectively, seem especially credible.

Some confusion is avoided if several forms of behaviorism are distinguished. *Methodological behaviorism* is a statement of research strategy for scientists that essentially says one can discover interesting, lawlike regularities by investigating the behaviors of organisms. It is fully consistent with methodological behaviorism that there could exist mental events apart from any observable behavior; such events would simply be excluded from scientific inquiry. Thus, methodological behaviorism is of limited philosophical interest. *Logical behaviorism,* which we shall take up later on, makes a metaphysical assertion as a general truth, namely, that mental events can be understood in a coherent way only if they are taken to refer somehow to publicly observable behavior. A still more sophisticated metaphysical thesis is *radical behaviorism* (Skinner 1974), to be discussed in the next chapter.

Other monistic theories attempt to slight the status of neither the mental nor the physical. *Identity theory* agrees that talk about mental events cannot be reduced to talk about brain events; it asserts instead that these two kinds of talk, though having different meanings, in fact refer to identical happenings—that the claim that mental events are contingently identical with brain events of the appropriate type is a coherent and empirically testable hypothesis. *Double-aspect theory* holds that the mental and the physical are different aspects of some third kind of substance; this theory founders on what that third substance might be like and how mind and body can be aspects of it or anything else.

Dualistic theories are conveniently characterized by the types of causation that each admits. *Parallelism* holds that physical events can cause other physical events and mental events can cause other mental events, but neither cause the other, even though certain mental events seem to be constantly correlated with certain physical events. But parallelism makes such a constant correlation a highly mysterious coincidence; in the absence of causal connections, it is hard to see why a broken bone might not correlate with pain one time and joy another time. Some philosophers have brought in divine intervention to explain the coincidence, but this is to offer an explanation even less understandable than the phenomenon being explained. Thus parallelism is usually rejected.

Epiphenomenalism holds that physical events can cause other physical events, and that some physical events (occurring in the brain) can cause mental events; but the mental events cause nothing. Epiphenomenalism seems to acknowledge our considered judgement that inner mental states are real occurrences, and that they are reliably correlated with certain physical events, while avoiding the sticky problem of how nonphysical, nonspatial mental events can cause physical events. But it ignores our equally basic considered judgment that our mental events, such as acts of will or deliberation, do cause things to occur in the world. It also requires relatively unusual laws of physicopsychic causality, since postulated effects come into being but play no further role in any causal chain.

Interactionism holds that physical events can cause both other physical events and mental events, and that mental events can cause both other mental events and physical events. This satisfies our considered judgment about the causal efficacy of our mental states but demands that we face squarely the puzzle of psychophysical causality.

Some of the above theories can be dismissed more readily than others. Behaviorism, interactionism, and identity theory seem to have enough initial plausibility to warrant further consideration.

3.3 Some Initially Plausible Theories

In determining which of the mind-body theories should be investigated in depth, we might ask how they would account for the placebo effect and which considered judgments seem to support them. To apply mind-body theories to the placebo case, we return to the formal definition of §2.3 and restate it in the form of antecedent and consequent events. The antecedent events are that the individual has a symptom, that he believes that he is in a healing context, and that he is administered an intervention. The consequent event is that the symptom is changed. An additional observation is that the change cannot be explained on the basis of specific properties of the intervention or of pathophysiologic laws as now known. The link between antecedent and consequent will generally be construed as causal, although this need not necessarily be so.[6]

Attempts to apply classical conditioning theory to the placebo effect (§1.5) suggest the possibility of a behaviorist account. Such an account would have to construe all the antecedent and consequent events in terms of publicly observable behavior. Problems may arise in two areas, however: giving a behaviorist account of subjective symptoms such as pain and believing that one is in a healing context. The usual method is to account for these in terms of dispositions to behave, such as, "I am in pain" means "I am disposed to yell, pull away, etc." If these strategies are acceptable, then the behaviorist account can be completed. Since behaviors occur within the realm of physical events, the causal connection between antecedent and consequent events presents no problem.

Causal interactionism views the placebo effect as an instance of a mental event (believing that one is in a healing context) and certain physical events (the intervention, the existing bodily state) causing another mental and/or physical event (the subjective and/or objective symptom change). This understanding of placebo effect entails causality between mental and physical events, an idea that needs at least some further explanation.

Identity theory essentially accepts the account given by the interactionist view, but adds that the mental events referred to are in fact identical to certain physical events in the brain; this identity eliminates the puzzle over causality. For research purposes, we would presumably want to learn which brain states are identical to the mental states referred to, so that we could study their connections on a neurophysiologic basis. We could then learn the precise nature of the causal network. Indeed, if this research led to our adopting new laws of pathophysiology, the placebo effect would cease to be unexplainable in terms of those laws and hence would cease to be the placebo effect as we have defined it. Given the methods of modern neuroscience, such a research program does not seem impossible.

Each of these three theories manages to account for the placebo effect; in addition, each can claim support for its account by pointing to basic considered judgments. One such judgment is that we rely heavily on the behavior of others to determine what thoughts, beliefs, and sensations they are having. Indeed, even though we generally feel that a person cannot be mistaken about his own mental states, we may on occasion reject his first-person report of them on behavioral grounds, as, for example, when a person, red in the face and with fists clenched, shouts, "I'm not angry!" Such a rejection lends support to behaviorism. Another considered judgment is that our increasing knowledge of neuroscience does in fact tell us interesting and informative things about the mind; in particular, it tells us that certain mental events are in some way dependent upon certain brain events. When an electrode is implanted in a selected brain site, for instance, it can reliably stimulate a feeling of pleasure or a specific memory trace. This considered judgment seems especially compatible with identity theory. Finally, interactionism is supported by the two considered judgments referred to earlier—that our inner mental states have undeniable reality and causal efficacy.

Thus, the three theories are each prominently but not uniquely supported by certain considered judgments. For the committed proponent of one of these theories, the importance of the considered judgments is likely to be exaggerated. Instead of being merely a prominent feature of what we mean by mental events, the considered judgment that supports one's own pet theory is likely to be seen as the crucial feature of the mental realm. Thus, it is important to subject these three theories to more critical scrutiny, taking note, especially, of the problem areas already mentioned.

3.4 REJECTION OF COMMONLY HELD THEORIES

Each of the three theories considered in the previous section either conflicts with other considered judgments or gives rise to troublesome conceptual puzzles. We will, it seems, have to look further afield for a satisfactory theory to account for the placebo effect.

Behaviorism holds that descriptions of any psychological state can be reduced to descriptions of behaviors that are, in principle, publicly observable.[7] Therefore, if we can find any psychological states which cannot be so reduced, we will have raised serious doubts about the docrine of logical behaviorism (how useful methodological behaviorism remains as a working hypothesis in psychology is a separate matter). To this end, let us focus on the mental-state report, "I believe that I am in a healing context," passing over for the moment the fact that our example is an abstract concept unlikely to arise in daily conversation.

Behaviorist accounts of belief states are commonly formulated as dispositions to behave or dispositions to make assertions. Our mental-state report might therefore translate as:

1. I am disposed to follow instructions given by the healer, to allow examination of my body, etc.
2. I am disposed, if asked, "Are you in a healing context?" or the equivalent, to answer affirmatively.

But these accounts as they stand are incorrect. I may believe that I am in a healing context but not be disposed to act in the appropriate ways if, for example, my fears of the medical procedures outweigh my desire to be cured. And I might believe that I am in a healing context but not be disposed to answer a question to that effect if, for instance, I have a desire to deceive the questioner. We could, it is true, expand our account to include such qualifiers: "disposed to . . . if I have no desire to deceive, if I understand the question put to me, etc." But such an expanded account is no longer behavioristic, since mental terms such as *deceive* and *understand* have crept into it. If in turn we try to give a behaviorist account of *deceive,* we will have to add similar qualifiers which include mental terms of their own, and so on. Thus it would seem that any behaviorist analysis of this sort will either be incomplete or will include unreduced mental terms in the analysis itself (Chisholm 1957, pp. 168–73).

Further consideration suggests that this problem reflects a general feature of behaviorism and is not the result of the particular example we chose. For instance, "knowing that..." involves being disposed to answer certain questions correctly if I want to, if I am not confused, etc.; and "wanting to answer," in turn, involves being disposed to answer correctly if I know the answer, if there is nothing else I want more, etc. It seems to be a necessary feature of psychological states that they can be characterized completely only in terms of their relations to other psychological states, although they can and indeed must be characterized in part in terms of observable behavior. Thus no psychological term can be characterized adequately in such a way as to eliminate all psychological terms from the explanation (Putnam 1964)—any more than we can describe the relation, "the tree stands to the right of the boulder," merely by describing the structure or the behavior of the tree itself.

If behaviorism must be rejected as an adequate account of belief states, we must also reject classical conditioning theory, with its simplistic stimulus-response characterization, as an adequate placebo explanation. This runs counter to the assertion that experiments showing a "placebo effect" in animals provide empirical support for conditioning theory (Byerly 1976). Can an animal believe that it is in a healing context? We can attribute to animals concepts whose presence can be manifested by nonverbal recognition: a dog can show by his behavior that he believes his master will be coming home soon (Kenny

1976, p. 51). But the concept of a healing context seems to be an abstract concept not open to this possibility. We must conclude that what was seen in the animal experiments was not the placebo effect as we have defined it. It may still be the case, however, that certain limited features of the healing setting can become conditioned stimuli, evoking responses in both animals and humans.

The problems with behaviorism are avoided by interactionism, since the latter theory explicitly includes mental terms. But interactionism gives rise to two problems of its own. One, already alluded to, is the puzzle of causality between the mental and the physical. We are used to accounting for causation in terms of one body's exerting a force on another, or in terms of transfer of energy. But if one event occurs in a body which has mass and can move through space, and another event occurs in something nonsubstantial and nonspatial, how can any causal connection exist?

The notion of *cause* used here is essentially Newtonian, and Gasking (1955) has suggested that this is not the primitive or the root meaning. The primitive meaning, he observes, is a recipe for producing a certain effect—*A* causes *B* when one can produce a state or event of type *A* as a means of producing a state or event of type *B*. The sense of *cause* that appears in the Newtonian or scientific context is properly viewed as a special case of this root sense.[8] But the price we pay for adopting a looser sense of *cause* is to give up the powers of explanation and prediction that accompany the term in its stricter sense.

Still, the causality puzzle might be tolerable if there were not another serious problem with interactionism. If I consist of a mind plus a body, and if thought and consciousness are properties only of the former, it is quite possible for me to conclude that my mind is the only mind that exists. I do in fact see many other persons, but I see only their bodies, never their minds; for all I know, they may be cleverly constructed automata which have no thoughts or consciousness. But certainly the idea that I could have grounds for thinking this runs counter to our basic considered judgments. It has been argued that I know others have minds by analogy from my own case, but such a use of analogy is inappropriate. Having seen, for example, the internal wiring and gears in many railway semaphores, I may conclude by analogy that the next semaphore I encounter will have such an internal structure. But since minds have no physical substance, I can never in principle check out my assumption about other minds existing, in the way that I can check out a railway semaphore (Ryle 1949, pp. 51–56). Interactionism, then, seems to relegate a considered judgment about which we feel firmly convinced (i.e., that other people have minds like ours) to the status of something we must take purely on faith and can never in principle be certain about. Any reasonably plausible mind-body theory that avoids this troublesome other-minds problem would therefore be preferable to interactionism.

Identity theory, in turn, avoids the problems that attend both behaviorism and interactionism, but it avoids these by postulating an identity relation that requires considerable scrutiny. An important feature of the identity relation is that anything that can be truly said of one term of the relation can be truly said of the other. We can say "the morning star is identical to the evening star," because any property of the morning star (size, position in space, etc.) can be truly predicated of the evening star, and vice versa. But the mind-body problem has arisen precisely because things that can be truly said of mental events (nonspatial, noninferential access to our own, etc.) cannot be said of physical events. We could try to reformulate our concepts of physical and mental events to remove some of these differences, but we would succeed only in either "mentalizing" physical events or "materializing" mental events (for example, by adopting a linguistic convention that allows us to locate mental events precisely in space). In either case, how one sort of event could take on properties of the other is as puzzling an issue as how the mind is related to the body; we would not, in sum, succeed in clarifying the mind-body problem.

Another feature of identity relations is that two things can be said to be identical only if they are of the same sort. This proposition follows from the way we define physical space—two things of the same sort cannot be in the same place at the same time unless they are identical. Two things of different sorts can occupy the same space at the same time—a tree may be in the same place as an aggregate of cellulose molecules. But in this case we would say that the tree is constituted by the aggregate of molecules, not that the tree is identical to it. For one thing, we can truly ascribe properties to the tree that we cannot to the molecules, and vice versa. We can, for instance, talk of the mean kinetic energy of the molecules but not of the tree. Also, the tree and the aggregate of molecules have different conditions for survival through time. If the tree is cut up into logs the aggregate of molecules survives but the tree does not; if the tree is pruned and the clippings burnt, the tree survives but the aggregate of molecules does not (Wiggins 1968).

Thus, for two things to be identical there must be some *sortal concept* that applies to both. For the morning star and the evening star, it is the concept *planet*. The sortal concept is important because it tells us where to look to see if the identity statement is true or not.[9] To see whether the morning star is identical to the evening star, we first trace one planet through space, then the other, to see whether we have traced the same planet or two different ones. But what sortal concept could serve this function for mental and physical events? It cannot be as vague a concept as *event* or *phenomenon,* because then we have no clear idea what to trace. An occurence, such as raising one's arm, can be viewed equally well as one event or many events, depending on our purposes (it could be one arm movement or the simultaneous contraction of many muscles). But if the sortal concept is made definite enough to trace through space or time, it would have to take on either physicalistic or mentalistic properties and hence would not apply equally well to the two terms of the identity statement.[10] We must conclude that the proposed mind-body identity assertion, despite its straightforward appearance, in fact conceals a number of sticky problems; it is not at all clear that the assertion is a coherent or meaningful one.

We have thus found serious problems with all three of the mind-body theories that initially seemed plausible. But this finding does not rule out the possibility that one or more of them could be modified so as to avoid some of the criticisms. By making some major modifications in behaviorism, on the one hand, or identity theory, on the other, one can arrive at a position called *eliminative materialism* (to be taken up in the next chapter) that agrees well with the considered judgments noted above and that is immune to several of the criticisms we have listed.

FOUR

Eliminative Materialism

Proponents of behaviorism and identity theory will probably reject the account of their theories offered in the previous chapter, objecting that I have looked at them only in their weakest forms. The theories, it will be said, have been so modified in recent years as to make them immune to refutation on the grounds I have mentioned. Here I shall analyze this claim in some detail, beginning with what I call *eliminative materialism*.

4.1 FEATURES OF ELIMINATIVE MATERIALISM

Eliminative materialism has developed out of identity theory and behaviorism, in response to some of the criticisms mentioned in the previous chapter. Identity theorists, noting the failure of attempts to translate mental-state talk into brain-state talk and observing the sort of ad hoc reformulations of mental and physical characteristics required to make the identity assertion appear coherent in its original form, have moved to a *disappearance form* of identity theory. According to this view, as we learn more about the neurophysiology of the brain, we will simply adopt the language of science in talking about our own internal experiences, and traditional mentalistic talk will disappear. Instead of saying, "I have a pain," we will say, "My C-fibers are firing"; talk about pains will drop out of our language in the same way that talk about demons has dropped out of our talk about disease. And the new language will offer greater economy, as the same terms which we use to describe our everyday experiences will also function in scientific observation and theory building.[1]

A similar advance has been made in behavioristic thinking. As operant-conditioning theories have become more sophisticated, views of what is to count as behavior have broadened to include various inner bodily states, and the past history of the organism has been taken into account along with present states. An example of such a sophisticated theory is the radical behaviorism of B. F. Skinner (1974).

A follower of Skinner, for example, would argue that in refuting classical conditioning as a plausible placebo theory (§3.4), we have in effect demolished a straw man, since psychologists have long since abandoned classical conditioning for the more refined operant conditioning. An operant-conditioning account of the placebo effect might go something like this. Suppose there is a certain internal bodily state (analogous to alpha rhythm, for example) such that the self-healing powers of the body work best when that state prevails. Achievement of that state will be positively reinforced by the quicker relief of symptoms likely to come from repeated exposure to the healing context. Thus, over time, the healing context itself might act as a stimulus capable of creating such a state in a properly conditioned individual. Relief of symptoms will occasionally result even if no active intervention is given. Therefore, instead of asking what circumstances are needed for an individual to believe he is in a healing context, we might ask what degree of *stimulus generalization* is present in the conditioning; the latter question is open to precise study and quantification.[2]

Despite important differences, it is useful to consider the disappearance form of identity theory and radical behaviorism together. First, it must be seen that the disappearance form is really no longer a form of identity theory at all. In the demon analogy, replacing demons as the purported causal agents in disease with a germ theory is not to say that demons are identical to bacteria; it is to say that, in the past, when we talked about demons, we were hopelessly confused, and we should change our account to reflect the facts as we now know them. In both radical behaviorism and the disappearance form, the suggestion is made that we *eliminate* our traditional mentalistic talk in favor of language that (it is asserted) is more scientifically correct. (Radical behaviorism gives new meanings to our present mentalistic terms and advocates retaining such terms in the language, but the change in meaning is so drastic that it amounts practically to eliminating the terms as we use them.)[3] The new language will be *materialistic*, as it will make reference only to physical states and events and will seek to explain human behavior in terms of deterministic laws akin to the laws of physics and chemistry: hence the title *eliminative materialism* for the combination of both theories.[4]

Eliminative materialism must be understood as a radical reconstruction of our notion of mental events, not, as in previously discussed theories, a mere explication. It is this radical-reconstruction feature that allows eliminative materialism to escape the criticisms leveled at behaviorism and identity theory in §3.4. Behavioristic attempts to deal with the problem of belief states, for example, failed because the behaviorist attempted to give an account that would capture all of what we presently mean when we talk of beliefs as mental states. And the identity theorist, in order to make his identity statement seem coherent, was tempted (vainly, it turned out) to impose mentalistic features on physical events, or physical features on mental events. By dropping mentalistic talk completely, the eliminative materialist can avoid being backed into such corners. The objection, "But what you have just described doesn't include everything that is included when we talk about beliefs (or sensations, thoughts, etc.)" is simply no longer relevant.

What the eliminative materialist proposes may be usefully compared to the idea of a paradigm shift in science (§2.1). For example, to say that chemists simply adopted a new terminology when they adopted the oxygen theory of combustion in place of the older phlogiston theory is to miss the actual extent of the revolution in thinking. There is an important sense in which the oxygen chemists were observing data and studying problems different from those of the older science. Furthermore, since one cannot work within a paradigm without accepting its set of basic presuppositions, cross-paradigm disputes are at least to some extent insoluble. Neither the oxygen chemists nor the phlogiston chemists could, in this sense, win over the other side by arguments about the superiority of their theory, since they would in effect be arguing about two different things; each side could accuse the other of question begging in the way they stated their theory.

Replacing "I am in pain" with "my C-fibers are firing" represents a similarly radical paradigm shift. For instance, if we were to object that I can be mistaken about "my C-fibers are firing" while I cannot be mistaken about "I am in pain," the eliminative materialist would reply that we regard incorrigibility as an important feature of mental events only because we are totally immersed in our present mentalistic language. Our objection is analogous to one the phlogiston chemist might raise: "Your oxygen theory is very nice as far as it goes, but it can't be correct because there is no room in it for the existence of phlogiston." Despite the problems of cross-paradigm debates, however, we will see if some telling points against eliminative materialism cannot be raised.

While eliminative materialism is a strong theory precisely because it engages in this radical reconstruction, its supporters may sometimes be tempted, as a debating tactic, to downplay this feature and to talk as if eliminative materialism were, after all, nothing but a minor modification of identity theory. If, in truth, the morning star is identical to the evening star, we have nothing important to lose by agreeing to call the planet by one name whether it appears in the morning or the evening; we do not have to give especially strong reasons for making this shift in language. Similarly, the eliminative materialist might play upon the confusion of the disappearance form with identity theory proper, to convince us that replacing "I am in pain" with "my C-fibers are firing" is a similarly innocuous terminological shift. But, as we will argue, we cannot let the eliminative materialist off the hook so easily when a radical paradigm shift is at stake. It will not do to say that elimination of our present mentalistic language ought to be carried out simply because such an elimination is conceivable.

Another point in favor of eliminative materialism is that the considered judgments listed in §3.3, which individually supported behaviorism, interactionism, and identity theory, respectively, combine mutually to support eliminative materialism. The theory accounts both for the emphasis on behavior in determining mental states, and the importance of neurophysiological discovery in elucidating the mind. And, assuming that the elimination of our mentalistic language can be carried out, we will be free to recognize the reality and the causal efficacy of the firing of our neurons. Furthermore, as already noted, eliminative materialism seems immune to the objections raised against the other three theories. Finally, and importantly from the medical standpoint, eliminative materialism, in calling for use of a more scientific language and for reduction of psychological explanations to deterministic and materialistic ones, seems consistent with trends in contemporary medical science.

Because of its sophisticated nature and the problems of cross-paradigm debate, it would seem difficult to launch a strong attack against eliminative materialism.

4.2 OBJECTIONS TO ELIMINATIVE MATERIALISM

Essentially two kinds of arguments can be raised against eliminative materialism. The first casts doubt on the notion that brain-state talk could readily replace mental-state talk; this type of argument does not directly confront the theory's radical feature: paradigm shift. The second does confront the paradigm shift, and asks directly what we stand to gain or lose by making it. In particular, we might challenge the materialist emphasis on the purported scientific advantages of making the shift. In line with our reflective-equilibrium approach, we might demand that moral considerations be taken into account as well.

Replacing talk about mental states with brain-state talk seems most likely to succeed if there is a one-to-one correspondence between brain states and what we now call mental states; at the very least, there ought to be a many-to-one correspondence, with any one of a set of brain states corresponding to a single mental state. But, at least with regard to intentional states, this "correspondence hypothesis" seems highly questionable. Goldberg (1968) takes the example "thinking about George Washington." Suppose a teacher asks three students to write down the name of the first president. *A* hears the question and immediately writes the words *George Washington*. *B* first has a mental image of the picture on the dollar bill, then recognizes it as the face of George Washington, and writes *George Washington*. *C*, having the same mental image as *B*, fails to recognize the person by name, and so writes down nothing. If we are asked which students were thinking of George Washington, we must say that *A* and *B* were. Although *C* had the right mental picture, we would not want to say that one can be thinking about George Washington and simultaneously not know that one is thinking about George Washington. At best, *C* was thinking about a picture of George Washington. But if we ask which students had the same thing going on in their heads (and presumably in their brains), the most likely answer is *B* and *C*. Thus we might well doubt that the relation between brain states and mental states is the sort to make the eliminative-materialist program plausible.[5]

Another line of argument can be raised against the suggestion that descriptions of the structure of the brain can replace psychological explanations with mentalistic content. Fodor (1965) argues that a psychological explanation must consist of both an analysis of behavior in functional terms and a description of the underlying structure or mechanism that makes the behavior possible. Describing the mechanism alone will not suffice, because for any functional description, an indefinite number of mechanisms are capable of producing it. For example, the firing of C-fibers is the mechanism corresponding with pain sensation in all human beings studied to date. But we could easily imagine some elaborate series of switches and wires that could be implanted in a body to serve the same function, and the number of different mechanisms we could postulate would depend only on our ingenuity. There is no necessary connection between the functional description and any one of these functionally equivalent mechanisms. Furthermore, a description of only one such mechanism would be merely a description of the interactions among the parts of the mechanism, and "would fail to describe the role of these interactions in the production of behavior" (Fodor 1965, p. 177).[6]

A moral consideration arises in regard to this point. We might imagine making contact with creatures from outer space who turn out to have psychological states analogous to our own, so far as we can tell from their conversation and other behaviors, but whose bodily physiology might be completely different. Are we to regard these creatures as our moral equals and accept moral duties not to cheat or kill them? Or do we regard them as wholly alien life forms, refusing to believe that they could have psychological states similar to ours because their structural form is so different? Eliminative materialism seems to steer us toward the latter course.[7]

But these lines of argument will be rejected as irrelevant by the committed eliminative materialist, who would insist that both the correspondence argument and the functional-explanation argument still misperceive the radical paradigm shift and reply to the materialist as if he were trying to give an explication of our traditional mental-state talk. Once the task is seen as one of radical reconstruction rather than explication, it will be seen to make no difference what the brain states correspond with or what form psychological explanations ought to take. Thus we have to face the materialistic proposal head on, and ask what it would be like to make the required paradigm shift. We can raise two problems: what sort of attitude we would have to adopt toward ourselves, and what sort of attitude we would have to adopt toward others. Following Wittgenstein in taking a language system to constitute a "form of life" (1958, I, 241), we could ask how the form of life under the materialist program would differ from our present one in these two respects.

Since talk in neurophysiology and in operant-conditioning psychology is essentially the talk of spectators witnessing an event without participating in it, the new life form would involve looking upon one's own inner states in the role of spectator only, or, put another way, regarding our present and future behavior in the same way that we regard our past behavior. This new life form precludes being an agent in the world and certainly undermines our moral thinking; in what sense can we be said to be responsible for our future behavior if we have no more control over it than we have over our past behavior? And to the extent that being a scientific observer presupposes the subjective experience and the agency of the "I" who is doing the observing, this life form undercuts scientific thinking as well (Platt 1972).[8]

The eliminative materialist might reply that there is nothing new about any of this. We have already been forced to reexamine our moral thinking as we became more knowledgeable about our conditioning by environment and early upbringing. But here the materialist is waffling between two positions: on the one hand he is claiming that his position represents a radical paradigm shift; on the other he is claiming that his position is merely a logical extension of features of our present paradigm. He cannot have it both ways. It is true, within our present paradigm, that we have had to reconsider the scope of our free agency in light of new knowledge of conditioning, unconscious impulses, and the like. But such a reconsideration still presupposes the possibility of free agency as a background condition. Without this condition moral discussion would simply make no sense. The radical paradigm shift would remove the very possibility of free agency; it would not be merely an extension of our present moral thinking.

Skinner is guilty of this waffling when he advocates reforming language by eliminating mentalistic terms such as *freedom* and *dignity,* and reforming life by more conscious use of behavior-modification techniques (Skinner 1971). This call for reform suggests a role for choice and action within Skinner's world view when in fact Skinner's deterministic metaphysics makes choice and action, in the sense that we speak of them, impossible. Skinner himself would say that if we accept his proposal we are not *choosing* to accept it: rather we are made to adopt it by a pattern of deterministic reinforcers. One might claim that this is simply "choice" and "free action" as interpreted within the new paradigm, but if so it is not at all clear that the new paradigm leaves any room for moral thinking.

These points are reinforced by looking at the attitudes toward others the new paradigm would have us adopt. Strawson (1968) notes two different types of attitudes that we presently adopt toward others under our present form of life. First are what we might call participatory attitudes, which are responses to the attitudes that others have toward us. These include such attitudes as resentment and gratitude, which in turn are closely bound up with the more general attitudes of moral indignation and moral approval. We also have what might be called objective attitudes, which regard others as things to be manipulated rather than as persons. Toward certain special classes of humans (e.g., small children and the insane) we have objective attitudes all the time. We also on occasion have objective attitudes toward some normal individuals, for purposes of scientific inquiry, for furtherance of policy, or simply as a respite from the emotional involvement that accompanies participatory attitudes. But, as these examples show, when we do adopt objective attitudes toward others, we do so for particular reasons.

Participatory attitudes, by contrast, are the norm for human encounters; when we have such attitudes it does not make sense to ask why. (That is, we might ask why one has one participatory attitude and not another—"Why did you have such strong resentment to such a silly insult?"—but not why one has participatory attitudes in general, instead of objective ones.)

Strawson then argues that a deterministic thesis, of which eliminative materialism is an example, would require us rationally to adopt objective attitudes toward all people at all times, in effect giving up participatory attitudes completely. But all interpersonal relationships as we know them, aside from purely instrumental relationships, are based on the participatory attitudes that make up the norm for our mode of life. To suspend all participatory attitudes as the deterministic thesis would require is to remove the possibility for interpersonal relationships. To think that we could even have a choice in this matter is grossly to misperceive the nature of our commitment to the form of life we currently live. It is to think that somehow the universal context of participatory attitudes can come up for review, in the way that we can review specific instances of application of these attitudes. We will, it is true, revise our attitudes toward a burglar once we learn that he was motivated by kleptomania, but we cannot in the same way revise our views on whether we should have participatory attitudes at all.

Strawson compares this commitment to participatory attitudes to our commitment to inductive reasoning (1968, p. 94). Could we give up inductive reasoning? Induction pervades our form of life, influencing us every time we pick up the phone when it rings, confident there will be a voice at the other end, and every time we turn the page of a book, confident the printing will continue on the next page. We could speak of doubting whether induction is justified, but this would be mere verbal expression of such a doubt; we have no idea how to live our lives except in a way presupposing the validity of inductive reasoning. But none of this restricts us from questioning specific uses of induction, or from trying to revise and refine our rules for applying inductive principles to specific cases.

But if this statement of the nature of our commitment to our present life form does not impress the materialist, let us suppose that we have somehow become able to make the choice between our present way of life and life under the materialist's new paradigm—the choice, that is, we have just argued is outside our ability to choose. We would then have to choose either to continue with our present life form or to make the radical paradigm shift. Presumably we would want to argue this choice on the basis of the gains or losses involved in the change, and presumably the eliminative materialist would want to argue that the gains outweigh the losses. But what do we have to tell us what counts as a gain and what as a loss, except the background context of our interpersonal relationships? Our notion of benefit and loss presupposes that background context. The materialist, for example, tells us that it would be more "rational" if we were to make the shift and adopt objective attitudes to the exclusion of participatory attitudes. But our concern must be not with what is rational in the abstract, but with what is to count as rational behavior toward others; and our interpersonal behavior is rational or not depending on the nature of our interpersonal relationships—it is rational to act toward my wife in ways that would be irrational toward a supermarket clerk. But again, our relationships presuppose the background context of participatory attitudes, of our attitudes toward others and others' attitudes toward us. It seems that the materialist cannot even join in this debate over gains and losses without implicitly accepting the framework of participatory attitudes and life form, which he is urging us to dispense with. This consequence, in turn, lends further support to our previous conclusion: giving up our commitment to this life form cannot be a matter for rational choice.

The eliminative materialist has yet another reply. All the talk about background contexts and forms of life has created a smokescreen around what the materialist originally wished to claim, namely, that when we are confronted with an organism whose behavior is determined in lawlike ways by its internal physiologic functions and the stimuli it receives from the environment, our attitudes toward it are rationally what Strawson (1968) calls objective attitudes, a conclusion which seems completely plausible. Furthermore, *rational,* a mentalistic term, has to be radically reconstructed to fit the materialist paradigm. Under this paradigm, rational behavior simply means behavior that enhances the survival probability of the individual or group.

As soon as we investigate the plausibility of this reply more closely, we find that it rests on the implicit assumption that our encounter with such an organism takes place as a special case against the background of our normal human relationships— indeed, that is the only way that we *could* conceive of such an encounter, given the human commitment we spoke of earlier. Thus, in understanding how we would react to such a case, we are dependent on the background context, just as we cannot understand kleptomania as a special case unless we first understand theft as a free action done for reasons and motives. Again, as Strawson says about our commitment to inductive reasoning, we can argue about the rationality or irrationality only of our judgments about specific cases. Our commitment to the universal background context of participatory attitudes is nonrational—it precedes and underlies our criteria for determining rationality or irrationality.

The eliminative materialist always has a final reply. Since what he is proposing is a radical paradigm shift, it is hopeless to argue with people who are so habituated to the old paradigm and its way of thinking that they can see no alternative. But, if we can force the materialist to adopt this as his final word, his position becomes much less plausible, for originally he seemed to be proposing not only that a radical paradigm shift ought to be made, but also, more importantly, that he could give good reasons for making the shift. If such reasons were to be both relevant and persuasive, they would have to bridge the gap between the two paradigms; they would have to show us, in effect, a way to make the transition in our thinking. And we have now seen that no such reasons are forthcoming. The reasons proposed are either completely foreign to our way of thinking and hence fail to persuade us, or else they are dependent upon our present paradigm and hence give us no reason for making the shift.

This conclusion can be illustrated by a diagram (fig. 4.1).

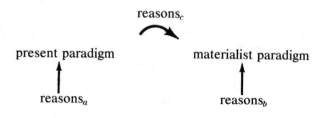

Fig. 4.1

We can give many reasons$_a$ to explain why we adhere to our present paradigm, such as pointing out how it allows for moral agency, and the materialist can give many reasons$_b$ for his paradigm, such as its usefulness in terms of psychological research. But reasons$_a$ and reasons$_b$ each show only the internal consistency of the respective paradigms; reasons$_b$ can never convince us to make the radical paradigm shift, and reasons$_a$ can never suffice to refute the materialist paradigm. If we could somehow imagine people who were living under a life form like that of the materialist paradigm, and who were considering the radical paradigm shift to our own present life form, our reasons$_a$ could never suffice to persuade them to make the shift, any more than the materialist reasons can conclusively persuade us.

The only reasons which speak directly to the paradigm shift are the "bridging" reasons$_c$. This sort of "bridge," we have just been arguing, does not exist—at least, nothing proposed by the materialist so qualifies. Although reasons$_c$ are the only reasons that could possibly show why we *should* make the paradigm shift, the materialist cannot speak to us of *should*. All he can say is that his paradigm is "rational" in the sense that it has survival value, and that groups that adopt the new paradigm will survive while those that adhere to our present paradigm will die out. But this is an empirical claim; all we can do is wait and see.

If the materialist, then, cannot give reasons for the paradigm shift, he can really say only two things about his proposal: first, that it is not logically impossible; and second, that as science progresses and subtly changes the way we look at and live in the world, such a shift may come to pass. But the same two things can be said about building a bridge to the moon. If this is all the materialist has to say, we may yet choose to make the shift he proposes, but it is then clear that we do not do it for sound reasons (i.e., for reasons$_c$, if any exist). At most we would do it as a strange leap of faith—strange because, unlike religious faith, the change undercuts rather than supports many of our most basic considered judgments.

This, then, concludes the various arguments that may be brought against eliminative materialism. The arguments have raised doubts about the theory, but have not refuted it—indeed, such a paradigm shift seems immune to refutation in any ordinary sense. Therefore, eliminative materialism remains a strong theory which we would probably be willing to adopt by default in the absense of any attractive alternatives. In particular, many materialists defend their views with special vigor because they feel theirs is the only realistic alternative to the troublesome Cartesian dualism. Formulating a theory consistent with all the considered judgments previously listed and free of the problems of eliminative materialism would eliminate this important reason for adopting eliminative materialism. To see what such an alternative theory would look like, it is first necessary to challenge some of the fundamental presuppositions of the Cartesian approach to the mind-body problem.

4.3 THE CONCEPT OF PERSON

All of the theories that we have investigated so far share the Cartesian assumption that *mind* and *body* are the two primitive terms by which other phenomena must be explained. Even though it represents a radical paradigm shift in other regards, eliminative materialism rests on this assumption nonetheless. It assumes that the realm of mind can be eliminated completely and that everything left falls into the realm of body. One way to begin the search for alternative mind-body theories, then, is to challenge this assumption, as, for instance, Strawson has already very effectively done in his essay, "Persons" (1958).

Essentially, Strawson's conclusion is that there are two kinds of predicates, *mental* and *physical,* and two kinds of entities, (mere) *material bodies* and *persons.* Only physical predicates can correctly be ascribed to material bodies, whereas both physical and mental predicates can be ascribed to persons. When one ascribes a mental predicate to another person, one does so in the same sense that one ascribes it to oneself, and the "I" to which I ascribe mental predicates ("I am in pain") is the same "I" to which I ascribe physical predicates ("I am six feet tall").

The important feature of Strawson's account is that the concept of *person* is logically required to be more basic than the mental and physical predicates ascribed to it. To see why this is so, consider the position of the other-minds skeptic that we encountered in discussing interactionism (§3.4). As a skeptic, I might want to speak of my pain, but I am reluctant to admit that there exist any other minds with pains of their own; all I can actually observe are other bodies, never other minds. Thus it makes sense for me to doubt whether anyone besides myself has pains.

But the coherence of this skeptical position presupposes that I have certain concepts. If I can speak meaningfully of my pains as distinct from others' pains, my concept of mental predicates must mean something ascribable in principle to a class: individual entities of the same logical type. I can ascribe mental predicates to an entity only if I can identify it as an individual, and I can do this only if that entity exists in the physical world. Thus, for anything at all to be the subject of mental experiences in the sense that my skeptical argument requires, there must exist individuals with the unique capability of having both mental and physical predicates ascribable to them, that is, persons (Strawson 1958, p. 342). Only by first having the concept of person can I move by abstraction to the concept of pure mind or pure consciousness (p. 341).

The power of Strawson's position lies in the fact that it is not an argument for the primitiveness of the concept of person. Rather, it is an explanation why no such argument is needed: to state his skeptical refutation of the existence of persons, the Cartesian dualist must presuppose the very concept he wishes to refute (p. 349).[9] Thus, by looking at the concept of person instead of mind and body, we avoid both a dualism in which two very dissimilar things must be brought together (interactionism) and a monism which seems to gloss over significant features of reality (behaviorism, identity theory, eliminative materialism). Moreover, if we accept Strawson's account as a very strong, basic way of refuting the Cartesian-dualist position, we have further grounds for refusing to adopt eliminative materialism. The materialist, after all, fears that allowing mentalistic terms to remain in our language would inevitably lead us back into the unsatisfactory position of dualism. But Strawson's powerful argument rests precisely on the logical features of mental predicates; losing such predicates from our language would deprive us of this very strong argument against dualism.

Strawson's account deals with the logic rather than the characteristics of the concept of person. The account is therefore of very limited use in elucidating the philosophical features of problems like the placebo effect. It can tell us, for instance, that the person who believes he is in a healing context is the same person as the one whose body undergoes change—that is, that the former is not mental substance while the latter is physical substance—and that is certainly something gained. But that multiple predicates can be ascribed to the same individual tells us nothing about the relationships among those predicates, if any; yet this is where the interesting questions about the placebo effect lie.

In addition, looking at our other considered judgments, we find that the concept Strawson has described does not fit well with our existing notion of person. We can truly ascribe at least some mental predicates, such as sensations, to many animals as well as humans. It is hardly consistent with our usual use of *person*, however, to call animals persons merely because we can ascribe sense-consciousness predicates to them (Frankfurt 1971). The next challenge, then, is to develop a concept of person that possesses the logical features noted by Strawson, but avoids some of the shortcomings of his position, while illuminating the placebo effect.

FIVE

A Theory of
the Person

Strawson's account of the concept of *person* (1958) indicates some logical features that a theory of the mind must possess to avoid both Cartesian dualism and reductionistic monism. The concept may be fleshed out in a number of ways, each yielding a theory of the person with distinguishing features. One such theory, to be discussed at length in this chapter, is based on statements about mind by Anthony Kenny (1973*a*) considerably amplified by Marjorie Grene (1976).[1]

5.1 THE CAPACITY THEORY OF THE PERSON
Essentially the Kenny-Grene theory, which I will refer as the *capacity theory,* holds that persons are animals possessing the ability to use symbols in special ways. The theory can be stated in terms of three major assertions, with some explanatory notes.

    1. Animals have capacities; different sorts of capacities require different sorts of explanations.

Capacity here is left essentially undefined by both Grene and Kenny, although we shall later consider some distinctions Kenny makes between a capacity, its exercise, and its vehicle. Grene gives three basic types of principles which may be used to explain various capacities of animals.

First, animals, as bodies in physical space consisting of chemical substances, obey the laws of physics and chemistry, and some of their rudimentary behavior can be explained in terms of these laws.

Second, animals can also exhibit goal-directed behavior which must be explained in terms of teleological organizing principles. We have already reviewed arguments to show that psychological explanations cannot be reduced to explanations of structure without function (§4.2). Moreover, even an inanimate machine, such as a clock, cannot be understood as a machine unless reference is made to such functional organizing principles. The laws of physics and chemistry can explain a clock only as a collection of masses and substances, not as a time-keeping device (Polyani 1958, p. 330). Grene further distinguishes first-order goal-directed behavior, in which an animal pursues a goal that is in effect already given, from second-order goal-directed behavior, in which the animal is able to choose among alternative goals. A similar distinction is made by Frankfurt (1971), who speaks of first-order desires, whose objects are to do or not to do certain things, and second-order desires, whose objects are to have or not to have certain (first-order) desires. Many animals have the capacity for the former, whereas only persons have the capacity for the latter.[2]

A third sort of organizing principle is not teleological in form, but normative or typological. A key example is the use made of species and species resemblance in biology. Here, explanations are in terms of adherence to or deviation from certain descriptive norms or types.

The basic point of this enumeration is the potential richness and variety of animal capacities. We come to think of animal capacities as a restricted class of phenomena by noting only capacities that can be explained by one type of principle while forgetting the applicability of other types.

>   2. Some animals have the capacity to acquire the
>   ability to use symbols in such a way that the use
>   confers meaning upon the symbol.

This description excludes computing machines, for example,

which are only able to process symbols whose meaning depends on outside personal agency. Grene stresses that this capacity is not in its nature different from other animal capacities; having this capacity is a special way of being an animal in the world, not something extra added onto the animal nature such that the animal is no longer "only" an animal. Kenny emphasizes that the notions of *symbol* and *symbol using* not only have fuzzy boundaries but are in fact infinitely open in a way corresponding to our use of the concept *mind*. What connects different instances of symbol using is a "family resemblance" as Wittgenstein used the term.[3]

Being a symbol user in this way has two important implications. First, an animal with this capacity is at least a potential dweller within a culture and a language system. Second, this animal, as Kenny points out, also has a capacity for responsible behavior. It is this capacity that allows one to choose knowingly and responsibly among alternative goals or actions not immediately present. Also, to use symbols meaningfully is necessarily to have purposes and pursuits, since, as Wittgenstein observed, meaning (for at least a large class of cases) is use within a language system, and language systems, in turn, constitute "forms of life" (Wittgenstein 1958, I, 43, 139, 241).[4] That is, the meaning of a word can be understood only by seeing how we use the word in our daily activities, and that use depends in turn on the goals and intentions of those activities.

> 3. Animals with the capacity to use symbols in this
> way are persons. To be an animal with this ca-
> pacity is to have a mind.[5]

In summary, then, having a mind is a special way of being an animal in the world—a way that entails participating in language and culture. In terms of the capacity theory, the notion of *person* cannot be grasped without realizing that it stands, in effect, with one foot in the biological realm and the other within culture and sociality. Our Cartesian assumptions tempt us to see in this disjunction two different parts of personhood; but since Strawson has demonstrated the primitiveness of the concept of *person,* we must resist this temptation to fall back into dualism and its attendent problems. It is not dualistic to recognize that different capacities of the person require explanation in terms of different principles.

The capacity theory might, indeed, be seen as a modified revival of double-aspect theory (§3.2). If "minded" refers to a certain capacity that an animal has, and "bodily" refers to its other capacities, then we have a way of making sense of a statement that mind and body are two different aspects of person. The difference, of course, is that originally double-aspect theory was proposed within the framework of Cartesian dualism—while not itself dualistic, the theory implicitly accepted the Cartesian formulation of the mind-body problem. The capacity theory, on the other hand, is a theory of the person with the logical characteristics proposed by Strawson's fundamental critique of dualism (§4.3). The concepts of "minded" and "bodily" as they apply to the capacities of persons are both necessarily derivative from the concept of *person* itself and no longer indicate a fundamental dualism. The capacity theory, instead of trying to answer the Cartesian question, tries instead to show that the question is erroneously framed.

5.2 THE CAPACITY THEORY AND THE PLACEBO EFFECT

As we have done with other mind-body theories, we must ask how the capacity theory of the person accounts for and illuminates the placebo effect.

As long as we had to deal with mind and body, we had difficulties bringing together the belief state of the subject and the changes in bodily condition, which, by our definition, had to be linked for the placebo effect to occur. Either a mental state had to impinge in some questionable way upon a bodily state (interactionism), or a mental state had to be reconstrued in different terminology, thus denying some of its crucial features (behaviorism, eliminative materialism). Furthermore, since the mind-body relation orients our thought toward the individual mind-body link, the crucial social and cultural dimension of human existence tends to be lost sight of. At best, this sociocultural realm comes to be seen as an extension of individual minds, rather than as in itself a central aspect of the human condition.

The capacity theory of the person changes the picture considerably. Our subject who experiences the placebo effect is no longer a mind and a body, but is a person. Being a person entails having all the capacities of a biological organism, and in addition the special capacity to be a symbol user and necessarily a dweller within culture. If being a dweller within culture is a special way of being an animal, it should not be anomalous if this characteristic were found to influence other animal capacities—including the capacities to undergo changes in bodily status and function. Symptom change caused by the placebo effect is therefore the bodily expression of the person's participation in the healing context understood as a culturally determined, symbolic phenomenon.

Of course, the mechanisms by which this symbolic-cultural event finds its bodily expression need to be studied empirically; the capacity theory cannot answer such questions on an a priori basis. The theory does suggest, however, that what is to be studied is the relationship between various capacities of the person, not relationships between two radically different substances or between two categorially different domains of meaning. We are still likely to need different explanations for different capacities—the physical-chemical laws which explain tissue damage, for instance, will not suffice for explaining how culture influences a person's belief states. Perhaps we will even have to develop new, bridging principles to connect different sorts of explanations before our account of the placebo effect will be complete. But this problem is quite different from that of relating mind and body as traditionally conceived.

The notion of the person as symbol user also suggest an additional sense of *cause* which may be operating in the placebo effect, and which has very different characteristics from the scientific sense of *cause* mentioned in our discussion of interactionism (§3.4). Kenny states, "To use something as a symbol and not as a tool is to use it in such a way that any effect which it may have on the environment lacks the immediacy and regularity characteristic of physical causality" (1973*a*, p. 47). Since using symbols in and on the world has definite effects even though *cause* in the physical or scientific sense is not applicable, we might want to speak of a sociocultural sense of *cause*.

Consider the way in which a No Parking sign might be said to cause certain behavior of motorists. Some motorists will inspect the sign and refrain from parking (in the vast majority of cases the inspection will take the form of an immediate recognition and not a train of reasoning). Other motorists, probably those most familiar with the neighborhood, will refrain from parking without even looking at the sign, and indeed without any overt or conscious awareness of the sign's existence. Some motorists will park at the spot, and of these, some will receive tickets, some will not. Some will engage in a sort of no-parking compromise, perhaps parking for briefer periods than they would otherwise.

Clearly the way in which the sign might be said to cause any or all of these is very different from the way in which the sign could be said to cause a shadow to be cast on a sunny day. Of the varied effects produced by the sign, none occur with the predictability or the regularity we expect of physical causality. And the sorts of things that would count as counterexamples for physical causality do not apply; even if there were cars parked by the sign more often than not, we would not want to deny its significance or its import. But still, all of the varied behavior that may occur, either conforming to the no-parking norm or deviating from it, is readily explainable. If more people park by the sign this week than last and fewer are ticketed, we might explain this as the result of a police strike. Our explanation would draw heavily on the past histories and prior states of the individuals involved and upon unforeseen present circumstances. This procedure fits well with the probabilistic nature of the behavior that we actually observe.

One might object to using the word *cause* at all in such circumstances. Don't these sociocultural cases (the sign "causing" a no-parking decision; an argument "causing" someone to change his mind) lack the constant, or at least statistical correlation between cause and effect that is a minimal necessary condition for ascribing causality? It is not clear that there is one central sense of *cause* such that this condition applies. Feinberg (1970, pp. 201–7) notes that purely empirical investigation normally yields an indefinite number of causal factors connected with an event. In giving a causal explanation we are forced to select one or a few of these factors, and the grounds for selection depend on our purposes in seeking the explanation. These purposes, according to Feinberg, may include satisfying our intellectual curiosity ("What causes the tides to rise and fall?"), making practical changes in the world ("What causes automobile fatalities?"), and ascribing moral responsibility ("What caused the death of the innocent bystander?"). Our purposes will determine the criteria we use to judge the acceptability of a proposed causal explanation.

Gasking (1955) claims that the "recipe" sense of *cause*, which corresponds to the second of Feinberg's three purposes, is the primitive or root sense. But none of the three purposes seems to be necessarily more basic than the others. The thought that there must be some root sense of *cause*, either Gasking's "recipe" sense, or the Newtonian sense, or some other, arises from looking at the causal ascription in isolation from the various human contexts in which it can arise. It is a mistake to assume that there must be some one common element, such as constant correlation, connecting all uses of *cause;* again, a "family resemblance" is all that is needed (note 3, above).[6]

The sense in which a culturally designated healing context can cause changes in symptoms is the sociocultural sense of *cause*. This is also the sense implied by the term *sociosomatic,* which Kleinman (1973) employs to describe medicine's "symbolic reality." Elsewhere, in a study of native healers in Taiwan, this author states:

> But our argument is that providing effective treatment for disease is *not* the chief reason why indigenous practitioners heal. To the extent that they provide culturally legitimated treatment of illness, they *must* heal (Kleinman and Sung 1976).[7]

Kleinman is referring mainly to the fact that participants in the culturally approved healing ritual will construe themselves as having been healed, even in the face of unchanged symptoms, as his data show. But some do have changes in symptoms, in a way not explainable by known specific therapeutic effects of the healing process. And for them the placebo effect has been caused in the sociocultural sense of the term.

Implicit in our previous considerations of the placebo effect has been the assumption that the placebo intervention works through mental routes in producing the effect. Because of the difficulties in specifying the nature of mental causation in a way that does not prematurely close off important avenues of research, we defined *placebo effect* in §2.3 by exclusion—as what remained after we had eliminated specific therapeutic effects and effects explainable by pharmacologic or pathophysiologic laws. The capacity theory places us in a better position to define *placebo effect* in an inclusive manner:

A placebo effect occurs for person x if and only if

1. x has condition C,
2. x believes that he is within a healing context,
3. x is administered intervention I as part of that context, where I is either the total active intervention or some component of that intervention
4. C is changed, and
5. the change in C is attributable to the symbolic import of I and not to any specific therapeutic effect of I or to any known pharmacologic or physiologic property of I.

According to this revised definition, research on the placebo effect would be directed at such questions as these: How can the symbolic import of various interventions be determined? By what mechanisms is symbolic import translated into bodily change (Levine, Gordon, and Fields 1978)? What accounts for individual differences in perceiving and being effected by the symbolic meanings of interventions?

Much of medical research has attempted to explain states of disease and health by looking only at the individual organism, just as Cartesian mind-body theories have attempted to explain mental phenomena by looking only at the individual mind or the individual mind-body dyad. A newer and very fruitful trend in medicine is to try to correlate the individual's social and cultural environment with health and disease (e.g., Lipowski 1973; Kiritz and Moos 1974). The revised definition of *placebo effect* places placebo research squarely within this new research program, a development whose research implications we will consider in more detail in §7.1 below.

5.3 THE CAPACITY THEORY AND CONSIDERED JUDGMENTS

In §3.3 we saw some of the considered judgments which individually support interactionism, behaviorism, and identity theory; and in §4.1 we saw that these same considered judgments jointly lend support to eliminative materialism, suggesting that the latter is a stronger theory than the previous three. We can now see how the capacity theory of the person matches up with these considered judgments, and also with some others that reflect our basic views of the mind.

Two considered judgments that support interactionism are that our mental states have an undeniable inner reality for us and that they have causal efficacy. Judgments that appear to lend credence to behaviorism and identity theory, respectively, refer to the importance of behavior and of neurophysiology in understanding the mind.

To see how well the capacity theory performs on these points, we need to introduce some further distinctions. Any *capacity* of an animal, like capacity in general, needs to be distinguished both from its *exercise* and from its *vehicle*. Kenny (1973*a*) gives the example of whiskey's capacity to intoxicate. Whiskey in the bottle has this capacity, but it is exercised only when the whiskey is absorbed by the body and interacts with particular cells. The vehicle is the alcohol in the whiskey—that by virtue of which the whiskey has the capacity to intoxicate. It is possible that another vehicle could be substituted; for instance, the alcohol could be replaced by some sort of stimulant drug. The capacity is dependent upon some vehicle being present, but not necessarily upon the vehicle present in a particular case.

A capacity has a real existence even though, when not exercised, it is in a sense invisible. This sort of "inner reality" is similar to the "inner reality" of the mind, of which we have an intuitive idea when we think quietly to ourselves. Since, given the proper circumstances, the invisible capacity can be exercised, its causal efficacy need not be questioned. In describing this capacity and its exercise, the capacity theory leaves us free to use our usual mentalistic language, as indeed we have already done by referring to the *meaning* of symbols. We are free to use whatever explanatory principles, mentalistic or physicalistic, best describe the capacity we are dealing with. On the other hand, eliminative materialism is able to accommodate these considered judgments only if we make the recommended paradigm shift and drop mentalistic talk completely from our language.

Knowledge of both exercise and vehicle helps us to understand capacity. Indeed it is generally by observing the exercise of a capacity that we come to know of the capacity in the first place. This explains why observing the behavior of others gives us good grounds for knowing that they have mind capacities and are persons. As Strawson notes (1958, pp. 343–44), being able to ascribe mental predicates to others is a precondition of their use, so our observations of others in everyday life "must constitute in some sense logically adequate kinds of criteria for the ascription." Furthermore, knowing more about the vehicle of the capacity adds an additional dimension to our understanding—how the capacity is grounded in the physical world, and how other factors in the world might alter it—even if knowing the vehicle is not our primary way of knowing of the capacity in the first place. Thus neurophysiology has a significant role to play in providing knowledge about the nature of mind.

But the capacity-vehicle-exercise distinction does not merely account for our considered judgments about the importance of behavior and neurophysiology; it also shows us where behaviorism and materialism go wrong:

> Behaviourism, when it takes the extreme form of identifying mind with behaviour, is a form of exercise-reductionism: treating the complex second-order capacity, which is the mind, as if it were identical with its particular exercise in behaviour. Materialism, when it takes the extreme form of identifying mind with brain, or with the central nervous system, is a form of vehicle-reductionism: reducing my mental capacities to the structural parts and features of my body by virtue of which I possess those capacities (Kenny 1973a, p. 51).[8]

Furthermore, noting that a capacity is dependent upon a vehicle but not upon a particular vehicle supports Fodor's (1965) argument that a functional explanation in psychology can be realized by an indefinite number of different mechanisms.

Since the capacity theory comports well with our considered judgments so far (not only establishing itself as an alternative to eliminative materialism but also, from the standpoint of our present paradigm, showing in its own way how materialism is incomplete), we might want to test it against other considered judgments about the mind. Recall that a general principle, to be acceptable, need not square exactly with our considered judgments; the principle can expand the content of our considered judgments if it can "extend them in an acceptable way" (Rawls 1971, p. 19).

One considered judgment worth scrutinizing concerns the possibility of the existence of disembodied minds. Given our present empiricist bias, such a possibility is troublesome, and theories, such as interactionism, that allow for it are suspect as a result.

The capacity theory eliminates this possibility. It is paradoxical to talk of a capacity unless it is a capacity of something—of certain kinds of bodies (i.e., persons) in the case of the mind capacity. Therefore the notion of disembodied minds makes no sense (Kenny 1973a, p. 49). Further support for this view is provided by looking at what it means to remember correctly, as opposed to merely seeming to remember. If I can be said truly to remember talking to Sam last week, it must be possible at least in principle to ask Sam, and for Sam to be able to identify me as the individual to whom he spoke. Since we already have noted that individuals can be identified through time only if they are embodied (Strawson 1958), we have no conceivable criteria for ascribing true memories of previous experiences, and hence continuity of experience, to a disembodied mind (Penelhum 1970).[9]

Another considered judgment concerns the central role that consciousness plays in what we mean by *mind* and also the supposed "private access" we have to the workings of our own mind. This judgment perhaps stands in need of some elaboration. Kenny (1973a) warns us of the danger of failing to distinguish sense consciousness from self-consciousness. Self-consciousness requires sense consciousness, but it also requires language: "one cannot know how to talk about oneself without knowing how to talk, and one cannot think about oneself without being able to talk about oneself" (p. 48). Here again one might refer to Wittgenstein on the impossibility of a private language accessible in principle only to one individual (Wittgenstein 1958, I, 243–363; Kenny 1973b, pp. 178–202). By pointing out that having a mind is having the capacity to use symbols, Kenny has established a feature of being a person more basic than self-consciousness. As Strawson notes (1958, pp. 337–39), the logic of mental predicates requires that they be used self-referentially in the same sense that one ascribes them to others; thus the ability to use these predicates self-referentially follows derivatively from the ability to use them at all.[10]

The problem of privacy or private access, then, arises mainly for sense consciousness or perception. Two points can be made here. One is that, with the switch in emphasis from minds to persons, the private-access problem loses most of its bite: "It is true that you cannot feel my pain or my pleasure or my hate or my love; that is true also about the pains, pleasures, loves, or hates of other animals" (Grene 1976, p. 191). The second point, following from this, is that what is distinctly human or "personal" is not having perceptions, but experiencing perceptions within the framework of self-consciousness and of language, a distinction that removes the private feature as a crucial characteristic.

> I will just say that the confusion seems to me to arise from people's being over-impressed with their ability to talk to themselves without making any noise, and their ability to sketch things before their mind's eye instead of on pieces of paper. I think that the acquisition of the ability to talk *about* oneself is enormously significant; the acquisition of the ability to talk *to* oneself is by comparison merely a matter of convenience. A society which differed from ours only in that everyone thought aloud all the time instead of thinking silently would be perfectly conceivable, equally intellectual, only unbearably noisy (Kenny 1973a, p. 48).[11]

In summary, the capacity theory accounts for the placebo effect in an illuminating way and also shows good fit with all the considered judgments that we have looked at. The eliminative materialist has the laudable goal of avoiding the problems of Cartesian dualism and of pointing out the importance of research into behavior and neurophysiology, but he feels that this can be done only at the price of a major paradigm shift to remove all mentalistic talk, and all moral and normative thinking, from our language. The capacity theory, on the other hand, avoids dualism and provides a secure place for behavioral and neurophysiological research, without requiring such a paradigm shift. On these grounds the capacity theory must be viewed as preferable to eliminative materialism and to the other mind-body theories listed in chapter 3.

5.4 PROBLEMS WITH THE CAPACITY THEORY

While the capacity theory of the person provides good overall fit compared to other mind-body theories commonly held, given the complexity of the mind-body issue it would be highly astonishing if the fit were perfect. Let us consider a few of the major problems that the capacity theory raises. The problems will necessarily be dealt with in relatively cursory fashion, as they lie on the borderline between philosophy of mind and other issue areas which are beyond the scope of this inquiry.

One objection to the theory comes from the eliminative materialist. It is not at all surprising, he would say, that the capacity theory explains so well the considered judgments that support materialism, since the capacity theory is nothing more than eliminative materialism in a new verbal guise. The three sorts of explanatory principles we have admitted (§5.1) are exactly the sorts that the materialist would use in explaining brain processes or behavior. The fact that we have admitted that the theory would allow certain very complex computing machines to be considered persons (note 2, above) would seem further evidence for this. If we can talk about the mind in such materialistic terms as capacity, exercise, and vehicle, we would seem to be carrying out the eliminative-materialist program; to claim that we are still leaving room for mentalistic talk in such a scheme is simply disingenuous.

This objection deserves to be taken seriously. We have,

after all, only cited Strawson's concept of the person on the way to stating the capacity theory; we have not proved conclusively that the capacity theory in fact adheres to the logical framework of Strawson's account. On more detailed analysis, the account we might give of the symbol-using capacity might in fact turn out to be reducible to purely "bodily" terms, and we will have indeed fallen back into an eliminative-materialist position, despite our verbal rejection of the Cartesian-dualist framework. If the capacity theory can be conclusively refuted, it will probably be on these grounds.

There are, however, two strictly intuitive replies to this objection that suggest that we have indeed avoided simply repeating materialism in a different verbal guise. One is the very prominent role given to language and culture in our account. Since this cultural dimension is basic to the understanding of *person* according to the capacity theory, but never arose even peripherally in our discussion of other mind-body theories, we have some grounds for thinking that the capacity theory of the person is indeed different in a fundamental way from theories arising within the dualistic framework. A second reply is the observation that, if mind is a special sort of animal capacity, we would expect to see a "gray zone" of capacities falling in between this special capacity and the purely "bodily" ones. And such a "gray zone" does in fact seem to exist, especially in the sophisticated behavior of higher mammals which resembles human behavior in many ways, even though these animals lack linguistic capacities. Indeed, it is precisely this "gray zone" of behaviors that gives behaviorism most of its plausibility as a mind-body theory. By contrast, had there been no such "gray zone" and had the special mindedness capacity stood sharply apart from all other animal capacities, we would have had grounds to suspect that a dualistic framework lurked at the bottom of our account.

There are, moreover, a number of assumptions underlying the materialist objection which are difficult to tease out. These assumptions have to do with questions like what it means to reduce higher-order explanations to lower-order ones, such as reducing the laws of psychology to the laws of physics and chemistry, what role free will plays in our lives, what sorts of scientific explanations of human behavior are compatible or incompatible with the existence of free will, what the relationship is between functional and structural explanations, and whether the former can be reduced to the latter without loss of content. For example, the materialist might argue that our present mentalistic language implies free will, that all three sorts of explanatory principles we have listed, if strictly construed, are compatible only with determinism, and so to argue that these principles suffice to explain mental behavior is the same as overturning our present mentalistic language.

The materialistic objection seems to me to be incorrect; but a complete refutation would take us far afield, into the metaphysical issues of free will and determinism and into the philosophy of the biological sciences. It is possible, nonetheless, within the scope of this paper, to make a few comments about reductionism. The reductionism issue might arise in particular from the assertion that the mind capacity is merely a special way of being an animal, not something above and beyond animal nature. This observation, in turn, is related to the distinction between first-order and second-order teleological explanations. But, if animals can have first-order desires while only persons can have second-order desires, aren't the latter different from the former in a more fundamental way than our theory would allow? Hasn't one in effect simply replaced the physical-mental distinction with the first-order–second-order distinction? This result gives rise to a dilemma. Either second-order desires are irreducibly mentalistic, so that listing them among animal capacities is mere verbal camouflage; or else we are engaged in a reduction of the mental to the biological.

When one attacks a theory as being reductionistic, one presumably has in mind a pernicious form of reductionism, in which an explanation in terms of lower-order principles succeeds only by ignoring crucial, complex features of the higher-order phenomena being explained. If one achieves simplicity and economy of explanation without dismembering the phenomenon in this way, reductionism cannot be faulted. The most common case of the pernicious form of reductionism is the proposal that mental processes are explainable merely in terms of physical and chemical laws. We have already argued that this proposal ignores the crucial features of psychological explanation (Fodor 1965), and that this form of reductionism will not work even for inanimate machines, let alone persons (Polanyi 1958). Malcolm (1968) has argued that if this reductionistic theory were true, no one could assert it to be true. An assertion is an intentional action, which implies purposive behavior and a belief state on the part of whoever makes it (otherwise we could not distinguish an assertion from a phrase being played on a phonograph record). But intentional actions lie outside the realm of deterministic physical laws. Thus the sentence, "Reductionism (determinism) is true, and I assert it to be true" is internally contradictory.

Since any reduction that is involved in Grene's (1976) list of explanatory principles is not of this type, the burden of proof is on the objector to show that it is reductionism of the pernicious sort (see Grene 1971). Certainly the second-order teleological principles differ in kind, not just in degree, from first-order ones; but as Grene has reminded us, we need different kinds of principles just to explain machines and lower-level biological organisms. In this regard, explaining how a person differs from lower animals is no different from explaining how a clock differs from a mere collection of metal and wood pieces.

Another problem with the capacity theory is that it seems to commit one to providing some account of how the mind capacity evolved or emerged from the purely biological capacities of organisms. Again, if such an account could not be provided, the assertion that having a mind is merely a special way of being an animal would be difficult to maintain. And the account is clearly problematic. Consider, for example, the difficulties in explaining how language could arise among nonspeaking beings; such beings, it seems, would have to possess the potential for speech at least in rudimentary form before they could discover language.

Two replies can be given briefly. One is that many purely biological characteristics of animals present similar puzzles for evolutionary theory. The other is that the really interesting questions of human evolution have to do with the stage after the mind capacity evolved. As soon as man developed language and culture, we became subject to two different kinds of evolution, biological and cultural, with the latter playing a dominant role in recent human history. To understand how a species can be subject to these two kinds of evolutionary forces, we require some concept of a being which is inherently both a biological organism and a dweller within culture. Thus, with the concept of *person,* we are puzzled by how mind evolved, but without this concept, we are totally unable to make sense of the history of mankind since its evolution.

All these problems connected with the capacity theory of the person are worthy of further study, and there is no compelling reason to assume that further study cannot provide some satisfactory solutions. Because of the many strong points of the theory (§5.3), its problems do not by themselves give us any grounds for rejecting it. Indeed the problem areas we have just noted give the theory a sort of indirect support. The fact that one cannot criticize the theory without immediately confronting significant issues in metaphysics and philosophy of science suggests that the capacity theory "covers the ground" well, and has the breadth that one should require from a comprehensive philosophy of mind. The types of issues raised by the problems above also lend indirect support to the reflective equilibrium strategy that we have been using by showing that one cannot investigate one area of philosophy for long without running up against others.

We are left, then, with a view of the person firmly grounded both in biological nature and in culture and language. So long as medicine makes progress by abstracting only the person's animal features for study, the dominant medical paradigm is bound to view the placebo effect as an anomaly. But the capacity theory of the person implies that no being can be *necessarily* both a biological and a cultural entity without the cultural features influencing the biological ones and vice versa (as the interplay between cultural and biological evolution illustrates). By this view, the placebo effect, in which participation in a specific cultural context produces changes in bodily condition, becomes an expected and understandable, rather than anomalous, finding.

In developing the mind-body implications of the placebo effect, we have relied heavily on the formal definition of section 2.3 as revised in section 5.2. We will find other features of this definition of use, as we take up the ethical issues related to the use of placebos in clinical practice.

SIX

Ethical Problems
in Placebo Use

Having devoted three chapters to the mind-body corner of
the reflective-equilibrium triangle mentioned in the introduction, we now come to the ethical corner. In this chapter we will
say little about the mind-body considerations previously
mentioned. We will, however, use the remaining corner, the
empirical-conceptual dimension of the formal definition, to
look at the ethical implications of placebo use. That definition
construes *placebo effect* very broadly—in particular, it
suggests that the term *placebo effect* is applicable even where
no placebo has been used. What implications does the logical
independence of the placebo effect from the use of an inert
treatment have for a discussion of the ethical issues?[1]

6.1 HISTORICAL BACKGROUND

How widespread has placebo use been in previous times and
did physicians in the past explore its ethical problems? At the
start of the nineteenth century, definitions of *placebo* similar
to the one now accepted began to appear in medical dic-
tionaries (§1.1).[2] Thomas Jefferson, in an early commentary
on placebo use in the United States, wrote to a physician friend
in 1807:

> To an unknown disease, there cannot be a known
> remedy.... Here, then, the judicious, the moral,
> the humane physician should stop. Having been so

often a witness to the salutary effects which nature makes to re-establish the disordered functions, he should rather trust to their action, than hazard the interruption of that, and a greater derangement of the system.... Or, if the appearance of doing something be necessary to keep alive the hope & spirits of the patient, it should be of the most innocent character. One of the most successful physicians I have ever known, has assured me, that he used more bread pills, drops of colored water, & powders of hickory ashes, than of all other medicines put together (Blanton 1931, pp. 198–99).

Jefferson went on to note that this was a "pious fraud," but much less harmful than the active treatments of dogmatic adherents to the therapeutic schools of the day. This apparent admission that there might at least be some question raised about placebos is somewhat unusual for that era; Thomas Percival's 1804 code of medical ethics, a voluminous and comprehensive work which dominated medical thinking for most of that century, is silent on the placebo issue (Percival 1975).

An early investigation into what would now be called psychosomatics included a review of how "Expectation or Hope" could stimulate the "beneficial Action of totally inert Substances" (Tuke 1873). Examples of the use of bread pills were given from both French and British literature, most notably a series of observations dating from 1845 by a British naval surgeon, reported by Sir John Forbes. While Forbes was enthusiastic over this remedy, Tuke added editorially:

Whether his advice has been adopted to the extent which it deserves, may well be doubted. Nothing can justify asserting what is not true in order to gain the patient's confidence—a course adopted in some of the foregoing cases—but this forms no essential part of the method of treatment now referred to. At the same time it is liable to degeneration into it (p. 371).

This commentary is ambiguous to say the least. I take Tuke to be presupposing a highly questionable distinction between outright lying and avoiding lying by judicious silence. Thus, he seems to be saying, if one tells a patient that a bread pill is active medicine, one violates a moral rule, but if one simply administers the bread pill, silently allowing the patient to assume that the pill is active medicine, one does not "assert what is not true" and so avoids blame. We will encounter a rejection of this moral reasoning below.[3]

H. C. Wood, citing Tuke's book approvingly, emphasized the efficacy of the placebo effect without expressing any ethical reservations (1880, p. 23). Samuel W. Gross (1887, p. 62) recommended placebo in the treatment of "psychical impotence from undue sexual excitement or emotional causes, ...since such cases usually remedy themselves." An early suggestion that one can obtain a partial placebo effect without resorting to deception by use of inert substances came from Shoemaker (1896):

> If the remedy be attractive in appearance and pleasant to the taste, it will be regarded as a signal success, even though of less therapeutic activity. An agent is sometimes given merely for the mental and moral effect, without having any medicinal action directly. Such a combination is called a *placebo*.... Although placebos are rarely resorted to, patients should always be well treated, and with a little care much can be done toward making preparations pleasant (p. 42).

Occasionally the medical writing of the period addressed the ethics of placebo use directly. An editorial in the *Medical Record* in 1885 (Placebos) defended an earlier statement on placebos against criticism from the *Peoria Medical Monthly* and repeated the position as follows:

> Physicians and intelligent laymen know that the former cannot always tell the plain facts to a patient

> without injuring him. It should be the rule of his life,
> however, to be straightforward and candid. There-
> fore, we say that placebos should be, and need be
> rarely, if ever, prescribed (pp. 576–77).

Going on to list the virtues of the ideal physician, the editors concluded, "We venture to say that such a man would not find it necessary to keep a polychromatic assortment of sugar pills in his closet."

The eminent Harvard physician, Richard C. Cabot, introduced his 1909 commentary on placebos in terms that contradicted Shoemaker's assertion that placebos were "rarely resorted to":

> Now, I was brought up, as I suppose every physi-
> cian is, to use what are called *placebos*. . . . How
> frequently such methods are used varies a good deal
> I suppose with individual practitioners, but I doubt
> if there is a physician in this country who has not
> used them and used them pretty often (p. 158).

Cabot wrote before the era when quantification became the norm in medicine; but a 1952 *British Medical Journal* editorial hazarded the estimate that 40 percent of patients visiting general practitioners in England were given placebo prescriptions (Bottle of Medicine).

Some sidelights on the extent and acceptance of placebo use in the nineteenth century are hinted at in some literary references. Louisa May Alcott in *Eight Cousins* portrayed a kindly physician compounding some bread pills for the heroine—to placate not her but her oversolicitous aunts. A very imaginative use of inert pills shows up in the first Sherlock Holmes adventure, *A Study in Scarlet*. The criminal, seeking revenge against two Mormons who had caused the death of his betrothed, fabricates two pairs of identically appearing pills, one in each pair inert and the other containing deadly poison. Certain of the justness of his cause, he plans to offer each of his victims in turn first choice of a pill, reserving the one remaining for himself. The first Mormon agrees at knifepoint to this plan and, having chosen unluckily, goes to his just reward; the second balks at this early form of the double-blind randomized trial and has to be stabbed instead (leaving the pills behind for Holmes to find as a clue). Doyle was himself a physician, but if he based this fictional incident on any real-life case, his biographers are uniformly silent on the point—despite the extensive commentary that has accumulated around nearly every other feature of the Holmes adventures.

6.2 ARGUMENTS FOR AND AGAINST PLACEBO USE

Although we have seen a few statements for and against placebo use from which moral arguments could be constructed, we have encountered no carefully worked out justification for either position, pro or con. A full argument is, however, contained in the work by Cabot (1909) already alluded to. Cabot (who among other titles held that of professor of social ethics at Harvard) discussed the placebo issue with a sophistication rarely matched by more recent writers.

Cabot dealt with placebos under the topic of deception in therapy, tying it in with deception in diagnosis (the inexperienced physician trying to create a false picture of competence instead of calling in a consultant when needed) and deception in prognosis (failing to tell the patient the truth about a grave or terminal disease). Cabot deplored the fact that "the great bulk of medical work, public and private, is still done by men—high-minded men—who believe that it is impossible to deal frankly and openly with patients" (p. 118).

Cabot dismissed the false moral distinction that I have inferred from Tuke by noting, "*A true impression,* not certain words literally true, is what we must try to convey" (p. 126). What counts as a true impression depends on what people reasonably expect from various types of social encounters, and from a physician the patient has come to expect an active medication. Thus the physician who administers an inert substance without comment, or with a noncommittal remark such

as, "Take this, it will help you," has created a false impressi.
and is guilty of deceit, even though he has not told an outright
lie.

To argue against placebo use, Cabot restricted himself to the
utilitarian form of argument—assessing the consequences of
actions—and avoided the deontological form—arguing from
preexisting duties: "You will notice that I am not now arguing *conseq.*
that a lie is, in itself and apart from its consequences, a bad
thing" (p. 141). He then listed some negative consequences,
both short- and long-term, that he felt outweighed any temporary good that could result from patient deception. The
short-term consequences are the loss of patient trust if the
physician is found out. He may in point of fact never be discovered, but "is it good for us as professional men to have our
reputations rest on the expectation of not being found out?"
(p. 133). The long-term consequences are the nurturing of un-
healthy public attitudes:

> The majority of placebos are given because we
> believe the patient will not be satisfied without
> them. He has learned to expect medicine for every
> symptom, and without it he simply won't get well.
> True, but who taught him to expect a medicine for
> every symptom? He was not born with that expec-
> tation. He learned it from an ignorant doctor who
> really believed it.... It is we physicians who are
> responsible for perpetuating false ideas about dis-
> ease and its cure.... and with every placebo that
> we give we do our part in perpetuating error, and
> harmful error at that (pp. 161–62).

Cabot concluded, "No patient whose language we can speak,
whose mind we can approach, needs a placebo" (p. 169). Instead Cabot favored taking more time to explain to the patient
the rationale for not using medication. The economic question
can be raised of whether this increased use of physicians' time
is cost-effective (Fuchs 1974, p. 125), a point we shall return to
later.

More recent articles (e.g., Bok 1974) do not go much beyond the arguments laid out by Cabot at the turn of the century. Recent advocates of more widespread placebo use have deplored the disdain directed at placebos as a wealth of new, scientific medications appeared on the scene (Benson and Epstein 1975). The most frequent argument given to support placebo use cites their undeniable efficacy and the advantages of avoiding the side effects of potent drugs (Sice 1972; Evans 1974). But these arguments ignore not only the negative consequences cited by Cabot, but also the deleterious side effects that placebos can produce on their own (Bok 1974) (reviewed in §1.2 above).

Another focus of more recent concern has been the distinction between *pure* and *impure* placebos, the former referring to totally (pharmacologically) inert substances and the latter to substances that have specific medical uses, but are used either (*a*) for a different condition, or (*b*) in doses too low to be effective. Common examples in today's practice are (*a*) antibiotics, thyroid extract, and vitamins (used in the absence of known bacterial infection, hypothyroidism, and vitamin deficiency, respectively), and (*b*) low doses of minor tranquilizers. A 1946 conference on placebo use (Conferences) disparaged the use of impure placebos while defending pure placebos. One participant stated:

> If deception is involved in the case of the pure placebo, it applies to only one person, namely, the patient, for the physician knows that the agent is devoid of all but psychotherapeutic properties. But when we use [an impure placebo] there is the danger of deceiving two people . . . . The doctor may come to think that the agent has potency when, in fact, it has none. That danger is real (p. 1726).

By this argument, deception of "only" the patient is morally unimportant, while possible self-deception by the physician needs to be guarded against diligently. The overriding concern is some principle of the purity of medical science. The academic physicians of 1946 were very much aware that they were witnessing the close of an era of ineffective or deleterious remedies endorsed by random or anecdotal experience, and the beginning of an era of new, potent medications supported by scientifically sound data. Any backsliding into the old, unscientific use of therapy was therefore to be stringently opposed. To this concern about scientific purity was added the observation that pharmacologically active agents, even in low doses, could be expected to produce more side effects than pure placebos. The conference concluded that (1) placebo use was to be encouraged, assuming "proper selection of cases and choice of placebo materials" (p. 1727), and (2) pure placebos were to be preferred over impure placebos. The problem of patient deception was thus implicitly dismissed as an issue.

A rather novel line of argument was suggested by Modell (1955, p. 70). Noting, as we have already done, that there is a placebo component in almost every use of an active medication by a physician, Modell concluded that since the placebo effect was already so widespread, physicians would be foolish not to put it to further use by prescribing placebos freely. Of course, this fails to take into account the fact that placebo use involves deception, while the placebo effect accompanying use of other treatment does not (a point we shall emphasize later).

6.3 THE ARGUMENTS SUMMARIZED

All the arguments cited above which favor placebo use are notable for the cavalier attitude they display toward patient deception. They are adequate reflections of medical attitudes in the 1940s, perhaps, but recent reconsiderations of medical ethics have emphasized the value of patient autonomy, the "contractual model" of the doctor-patient relationship, and the right of informed consent (Ramsey 1970; Veatch 1972; Fried 1974; Brody 1976).

The importance of informed consent in research on human

subjects has been almost universally recognized (Freund 1969). In most instances, patients can be informed when the design of the experiment involves placebo use. So long as the protocol is double-blind, so that the individual subject does not know if he is receiving placebo or experimental drug, the scientific validity of the experiment should not be altered by imparting this general information (Bok 1974).[4] An inability to get people to volunteer for some experiments would, admittedly, constitute a practical problem; placebo surgery might be a case in point (Beecher 1961).

In contrast to the experimental use of placebos stands the therapeutic use in which the hoped-for beneficial effects are intended directly and solely for the patient. The arguments given above in favor of placebo therapy might be reconstructed as follows:

1. A physician ought to employ any remedy which provides significant possibility of benefit while imposing only minimal medical risks on the patient.[5]
2. Placebos offer significant possibility of benefit while imposing only minimal medical risk.
3. Therefore, physicians ought to employ placebos.

This argument makes no distinction between remedies that rely for their success on patient deception and those that do not.[6] The deception issue is important particularly because "significant benefit" and "minimal risk" are value judgments. If informed of the nature of the therapy, the patient can have at least some say as to what is acceptable risk and benefit for him; if deceived, the patient is totally dependent on the judgment of the physician, who may not share the patient's values and preferred lifestyle.

The defender of placebo use, if deontologically inclined, might argue that the deception involved is not "really" deception but rather is on the order of a white lie (Bok 1974). Some justification for this might come from noting that the physician after all, acting for the patient's benefit and not for any selfish motive. Or, if inclined toward utilitarianism, the fender might claim that deception involves significant damage only if the physician is found out, and the chances of this are small enough so that the good to be gained from placebo use outweighs the potential harm.[7] But neither of these replies takes into account the importance of patient self-determination and autonomy.

An additional implication of placebo deception not dealt with so far is the financial cost of the prescription. Presumably, unless the patient is billed for an amount commensurate with the cost of active drugs, the deception will not succeed. But is it ethical to charge for sugar pills what one would charge for an antibiotic or a tranquilizer? Further, the empirical studies of the placebo effect suggest that increasing the cost of the prescription, making the remedy seem more valuable and exotic, will enhance the placebo effect. Should this be done in practice? If so, should the extra sum go to the pharmacist, the physician, or some favorite charity? Should the price be raised even higher for richer patients? If so, are the poor being deprived of a possibly effective remedy? Should private or government-funded medical insurance pay for the difference? The medical literature has been largely silent on these issues, but they would have to be addressed as part of any serious defense of placebo use.

Arguments against placebo use, we find, also display deontological and utilitarian variants. The former might run:

1. It is wrong to deceive someone knowingly (except in extreme circumstances, as when the SS troopers ask about Jews hidden in the attic).
2. The therapeutic use of placebos requires deception.
3. Therefore, the therapeutic use of placebos is wrong.

The utilitarian argument against placebo use is well laid out by both Cabot (1909) and Bok (1974):

1. A policy should be adopted only if it decreases

the net amount of pain and suffering, taking into account both the short- and long-range consequences.

2. Regular use of placebos by physicians will relieve the symptoms of many patients. In some cases these symptoms will have been severe; but in many if not in most cases they will have been short-lived or trivial. Placebos will thus directly produce some diminution of pain and suffering.

3. In the few instances where the patient discovers the deception, his consequent loss of faith in the physician will seriously hamper any further therapeutic attempts. This result will produce some short-term increases in pain and suffering.

4. In the long term, it will probably become generally believed that physicians deceive. This opinion will lead to a slight but generalized mistrust of physicians, hampering some of their therapeutic activities. The entire population is likely to experience a considerable increase in pain and suffering.

5. Also in the long run, the public attitude will be reinforced that symptomatic relief with active drugs is the best treatment for all ills. This perception is likely to lead to overuse of medications, with increased morbidity and mortality from adverse drug reactions. It will also interfere with patients' learning rational health habits that could better prevent disease. Again taking into account the total population, a large increase in pain and suffering can be predicted.

6. The increases in pain and suffering in situations 3–5 are likely to outweigh the diminution in pain and suffering in number 2.

7. Therefore, a policy of placebo use cannot be justified.

Although this utilitarian argument makes of number of empirical assumptions which need to be tested in practice, none of them seem unreasonable.

The deontological argument against placebo use would prohibit this practice in all but the most extreme circumstances (such as, perhaps, an irrational patient threatening immediate suicide). The utilitarian argument, however, addresses only placebo use as a general policy and leaves open the possibility of justifying very limited use in selected cases. This matter requires further consideration.

6.4 LIMITED PLACEBO USE

Many of the arguments we have previously reviewed dealt with placebo use generally. Some medical authors, however, many of whom at least implicitly recognize the ethical problems associated with deception, still feel that placebos have a particular utility in specific categories of cases, and that their limited use can be justified on those grounds. Suggested specific indications for placebos include the following:

1. diseases for which placebos have proved efficacious experimentally (Bourne 1971);
2. diseases for which no pharmacologically active treatment exists (Frank 1974);
3. cases of narcotic withdrawal in which placebo can be substituted gradually for the narcotic (Leslie 1954; Wolf 1959);
4. instances of necessarily prolonged diagnostic testing, during which the patient, if not placated by "treatment," might become dissatisfied and not return for needed therapy (Leslie 1954);
5. anxiety states which appear to be interfering with the success of other, essential treatment (Frank 1974);
6. illnesses for which no drug or other treatment is indicated, but for which the patient demands treatment (Bourne 1971);

7. temporary situations in which placebos are used
   initially to placate the patient until a doctor-
   patient relationship can be established for more
   direct use of psychotherapy or emotional support
   (Wolf 1959; Frank 1974).

Several of these indications can be readily dismissed. In (1),
limiting placebo use to those symptoms for which experimental
efficacy has been demonstrated is tantamount to not limiting
placebo use at all (§1.2). In (3), placebos have proved in some
patients to be every bit as addicting as narcotics (Bourne 1971;
Bok 1974). In (5), why should anxiety states be singled out for
placebo use, when both pharmacologically active anti-anxiety
drugs and anxiety-lowering psychotherapeutic techniques are
readily available?

In (6) a more serious question is raised. Sometimes a patient
may seem to be asking for a placebo ("I know that you say
drugs won't help me, Doc, but surely you can give me *something*"). Assuming that there are sound reasons not to use
placebos in general, does such a case differ materially from
that of a patient insisting that he wants a gall bladder operation
despite repeated reassurances about the absence of disease in
that organ? If the patient is fully informed about risks and
benefits (or indicates a desire not to be so informed), how far is
the physician obligated to go in satisfying desires contrary to
his own views of proper medical practice or of medical ethics?
This is an important issue that must be addressed by any contractual view of the doctor-patient relationship, but it is not
peculiar to the placebo case.

Of all the indications, (7) may be most acceptable because of
its temporary nature and the fact that temporary deception is
to be used as a means for achieving a state in which deception
is no longer necessary. But even this sort of use raises questions, including whether upon establishing the hoped-for relationship, the fact that a placebo has been used is to be revealed to the patient. Bourne (1971) comments somewhat
obscurely on this point:

> If the relationship between the physician and the patient is a strong one, the true nature of the placebo can be revealed at a later date with little danger. If such a relationship does not exist, the placebo should not have been administered in the first place (p. 4).

This way of putting it seems to require clairvoyance on the part of the physician beginning treatment. What Bourne seems to be saying is that if the initial relationship is so shaky that the doctor feels the need to resort to placebos, the likelihood of a strong future relationship is very low. In addition, what sort of relationship would arise in (7)? If it is one in which the patient expects the doctor to react to each new symptom with another drug, more harm than good may have been done, as Cabot noted.

With placebos, of course, as with any other proposed medication, a final answer on the appropriateness of use or nonuse cannot be given until alternative modes of therapy have been evaluated. And most writers on the placebo effect have made little explicit mention of the alternatives (again Cabot is the notable exception). This matter now requires consideration.

6.5 Alternatives to Placebos

Demonstrating that there are acceptable alternatives to using placebos as a general policy does not rule out the possibility that in a few specific instances there will be no practical alternative to placebo use. Consider, for example, the physician called to the bedside of a patient who is in great pain, who is known to be allergic to all available analgesic drugs, and who speaks a foreign tongue for which no fluent interpreter is available. Both deontological and utilitarian defenses could be given for placebo use in such extreme circumstances. The deontologist might propose that the patient has a right to relief from suffering which overrides the physician's duty not to deceive; any of us, in the patient's place, would prefer deception to continued agony. The utilitarian might note, on the one hand, the great net increase in good over evil available to that patient and, on the other hand, the absence of the negative consequences attendant upon adopting placebo use on a wide-spread basis. But, one hopes, the very implausibility of this example suggests that such situations will be quite rare.

If it could be shown that in general, attractive alternatives to placebo use exist, then the burden of proof would fall upon the placebo user; he would be obliged to show that some special, overriding circumstances apply in the case at hand.

In addressing alternatives, we must overcome a serious medical bias. Physicians are likely to consider as viable alternatives only other drugs, surgery, and similarly inter-ventionist modalities, especially those involving manipulating the patient's body. They are likely to reject talking with the patient, providing education or emotional support, or watchful waiting—"doing nothing" or "sitting on one's hands" (Ben-jamin 1976). Thus most of the medical discussions of placebos cited so far implicitly assume that placebos provide the only alternative to doing nothing (or having the patient seek another doctor).

It is on the matter of alternatives that our formal definition of *placebo effect* (§2.3) proves most illuminating for the ethical issue. After considering various limiting cases in §2.2, we were led to adopt a definition of *placebo effect* which did not contain the term *placebo*. On this conceptual basis, we established that using placebos is only one means for eliciting the placebo effect—that the latter, in fact, pervades most of medical prac-tice even where the former are seldom if ever used.[8] Whereas Modell (1955) notes how widespread the placebo effect is and relies on this fact to justify the use of placebos, we may draw the opposite conclusion: since the placebo effect can be elic-ited by other, nondeceptive means, placebos need not be re-sorted to.

A practical model of how the placebo effect (by our broadened definition) can be induced without any sort of de-ception is provided by a study entitled "Reducion of Post-

operative Pain by Encouragement and Instruction of Patients"
(Egbert et al. 1964). While a control group of surgical patients
received routine care, the randomly selected experimental
group received a special preoperative visit from the anesthe-
siologist, who discussed the nature of postoperative pain
and instructed the patient on relaxation and postural methods
to minimize it. The surgeons (who were unaware that the
study was being conducted) ended up giving the experimental group half as much narcotic and discharging them two
days earlier from the hospital, on the average, as compared to
the control patients.

Writing some years before Adler and Hammett's 1973 paper,
Egbert and coworkers anticipated nicely the meaning model of
the placebo effect (§1.5):

> We believe that our discussions with the patients
> have changed the meaning of the postoperative
> situation for these patients. By utilizing an active
> placebo action, we have been able to reduce their
> postoperative pain (p. 826).

Specifically, for these patients the idea of not-talked-about
pain which one had to lie back and endure had changed to the
idea of predictable pain which one could control by learned
measures.[9]

One example such as the Egbert study, however, might not
assure skeptics that alternatives to placebo use exist in a wide
enough variety of cases. Therefore it may be useful to return to
the seven specific indications for placebos suggested by medical authorities (§6.4). If in each we can suggest ways of eliciting
the placebo effects without using placebos, we might conclude
that the alternative modes might well work in other instances
also, where the desirability of placebo use from the medical
standpoint is less clear. (We can eliminate [1], which was
shown to be tantamount to unlimited placebo use.)

2. No active treatment. There is almost no disease for which
supportive care and compassionate concern cannot contribute

to the patient's comfort, even where cure is impossible. Further, to give placebos to make the patient think that cure is possible is to deceive the patient not only about the treatment but also about the prognosis (see Cabot 1909, pp. 138–57).

3. Narcotic withdrawal. The medical management of withdrawal symptoms, including temporary substitution of less addicting drugs (such as methadone for heroin), is well developed. Psychotherapy to remove emotional need for the drug is much less successful; but placebo use, reinforcing the drug-taking habit as a way of dealing with life's stress, hardly seems any more helpful.

4. Prolonged diagnostic testing or uncertain diagnosis. The doctor can level with the patient about what is known so far and what isn't; when some potentially serious diseases have been ruled out, he can give reassurance on that score ("At least we know now it isn't cancer"). What discourages the patient is probably not the uncertainty so much as the suspicion that he is getting a "runaround" from the physician.

5. Anxiety. A number of specific anti-anxiety drugs, and short- and long-term psychotherapy are all available to deal with this problem.

6. Patient demands treatment when none indicated. This situation is difficult. The demand may be symptomatic of an underlying emotional problem, such as excessive dependency needs or denial of the true nature of the illness (especially if the patient secretly fears that the illness is psychological). If these deeper problems can be confronted, the strategy of making the patient feel more in control can be especially useful (Cassell 1976).

7. Temporary use. Instead of using some temporary means until a trusting relationship is established, why not speed up the establishment of the relationship? In general the physician who takes time to hear the patient's true concerns, responds frankly to questions, and indicates to the patient what he can expect in the future, establishes considerable trust almost immediately.

Two rebuttals to the above examples suggest themselves. One is that the alternative techniques described have a high failure rate under the day-to-day pressures of medical practice, when the physician cannot always appear as unhurried and as compassionate as he would like. Two replies are clear from chapter 1: placebos generally have only a 30 to 40 percent success rate in most studies; and a placebo is still less likely to work if the physician who administers it does not display compassion and concern.

The second rebuttal is the already familiar matter of the cost-effectiveness of spending more time with patients. In the absence of solid data, one may assume that establishing trust and teaching the patient more control over his own body takes quite a bit longer than writing a prescription for sugar pills or injecting some vitamin B_{12} (Fuchs 1974, p. 125). But one may also assume that communication with and education of the patient is in some sense an investment for the future: the informed patient may handle subsequent symptoms with minimal medical attention, whereas the patient given placebos will continue to come back for more and different placebos. Furthermore, current strategies toward patient education emphasize the role to be played by nurses and other health professionals to minimize the time required for physician contact.

Summarizing our argument so far, we have not created an absolute moral prohibition against placebo use, but we have established a prima facie presumption against it, placing the burden of proof back on the user. Our position has both a deontological and a utilitarian rationale. Deontologically, not deceiving is preferable to deceiving. Assuming that the two techniques in general are equally effective,[10] we can compare the consequences of placebo use to eliciting the placebo effect by nondeceptive means from a utilitarian standpoint. The nondeceptive means eliminate all the negative consequences listed by Cabot and Bok (§6.3). Since nothing has been concealed in the first place, the patient cannot discover later that he has been deceived; hence, the general public can never come to suspect that doctors routinely deceive people. And greater patient education, far from promoting self-perpetuating, counterproductive health habits, is likely to have the opposite effect; in the long run this approach may in fact prove far more cost-effective than acute illness care (Kristein, Arnold, and Wynder 1977).[11]

There is yet an additional dimension to this line of argument, arising from the notion of the person that we developed in §5.1. Being a person necessarily involves a capacity for autonomous, responsible behavior. If we are concerned about the actualization and not just the mere existence of our human capacities, we seek to maximize responsible behavior; deceptive practices, which deprive us of the information we might need to make decisions in a responsible way, are thus to be avoided. Indeed, it seems that placebo use could never have become ingrained in medical practice had not physicians (with the tacit acquiescence of patients) developed a general approach of treating patients as nonpersons in this sense, on the assumption that patients cannot understand technical medical information and are too emotionally distraught by illness to behave responsibly.[12]

SEVEN

Research and
Therapeutic Implications

Any philosophical inquiry into medical matters will be judged partly by whether it suggests opportunities for empirical research and eventually for treatment applications. Our examination of the research and therapeutic implications of our study will emphasize two lessons drawn from the foregoing material: first, our appreciation of the sociocultural and symbolic dimensions of the placebo effect, and second, the ethical importance of patient autonomy and the possibility of nondeceptive alternatives to use of placebos. An elaboration of the meaning model of placebo action, first mentioned in §1.5, will serve as our first guide for further research.

7.1 THE MEANING MODEL

Among several proposed theories of placebo action reviewed in §1.5, the meaning model of Adler and Hammett (1973) comes closest to encompassing the essential features arising from our discussion. In this model, the subjective sense of *meaning* in the illness experience is factored into (1) *system formation,* or the providing of a coherent explanation of the illness consistent with the patient's world view, and (2) *group formation,* or the gathering of a supportive, caring group around the patient. Together, these factors "are invariably used in all successful interpersonal therapies, and are the necessary and sufficient components of the placebo effect"

(Adler and Hammett 1973, p. 597). By *system formation* these authors indicate the cultural-symbolic realm whose importance we have stressed; and by *group formation* they point to sociological insights into the workings of the sick role.[1] Thus, the model directs research toward cultural and social aspects of human nature.

The meaning model provides an important corrective for the bulk of placebo research on personality variables, which has focused almost exclusively on the emotional states of subjects without looking at their assumptions or systems of belief.[2] Two cases suggest the central role that belief systems can play in the placebo effect:

> CASE 1. A woman of Christian Science faith failed to heal despite the relative simplicity of the surgical procedure [to correct retinal detachment]. Afterwards, she indicated to the surgeon that having surgery was in conflict with her Christian Science beliefs. Before reoperating, the surgeon made clear to her that he was only doing a mechanical task akin to realigning a broken bone, and that her faith was the major factor in the actual healing. His statement helped her to reconcile her Christian Science beliefs with the necessity of surgery, and she healed quickly after the second operation (Mason et al. 1969, p. 139).

> CASE 2. A man with far advanced lymph node malignancy, and with readily palpable, large tumor masses in the neck, abdomen, and groins, learned of the appearance of a new "miracle cancer drug," Krebiozen, in the newspapers. At his insistence he was included in a clinical trial of the drug, against protocol regulations, since his physicians felt that he had no more than two weeks to live. Within ten days he had demonstrated marked regression in the size of the tumors; and where he had previously been bedridden and gasping for air, he was well enough to be discharged from the hospital. After two months,

however, news reports began to circulate carrying more discouraging news about Krebiozen, and the patient returned to the hospital with return of symptoms and recrudescence of his tumor masses. The physician then announced that it had been discovered that the first batches of Krebiozen had deteriorated with storage, and that a shipment of more potent drug was about to be received. He then proceeded to give the patient injections of plain water. Again, in a short time, the tumors shrank and the patient had nearly total symptom relief.

The patient remained healthy after this for some months until another news report appeared: "Nationwide AMA tests show Krebiozen to be worthless as cancer treatment." Within a few days the patient was readmitted, very depressed, and with far advanced symptoms; he died less than two days later (condensed from Klopfer [1957]).

Without question the emotional states of the two patients above played a large, if not crucial, role in the clinical outcomes. The point is, however, that descriptions which include reference only to emotional states cannot do full justice to the cases. For example, case 2 could be described as an example of the disappearance and reappearance of cancer symptoms and signs corresponding with cyclic depression. But such a description, making no reference to the changes in cognitive states which precipitated the depressions, is an unsatisfactory explanation. *Meaning* explanations, as we shall consider in more detail in the section on therapy, can often give much more specific clues on how to intervene for the patient's benefit.

The focus on meaning indicates a further need for cross-cultural studies of the placebo effect and the healing context. To my knowledge, anthropologists have not carried our cross-cultural studies of the placebo effect as a distinct phenomenon, even though their studies of culturally related medical practices in general have provided valuable clues into the workings of the placebo effect (e.g., Kleinman and Sung 1976). As we have already shown, however, what counts as a healing context can be expected to be different from culture to culture. Of special interest is the conflict produced by the introduction of Western scientific medicine into a traditional culture; if both scientific and traditional medicine rely on the placebo effect for much of their efficacy, scientific medicine might be expected to show a clear superiority "only to the extent that scientism has become a successful ideology" within that culture (Riley 1976). Furthermore, understanding the meaning of illness within a culture and the social-stabilizing functions of healing practices within a society are essential in order to compare the efficacy of medical-care systems; what one defines as disease and what one considers to be control over disease can be expected to vary from culture to culture (Fabrega 1976).

In medicine, the diagnosis is the primary mechanism for conferring meaning upon an illness event. While medical thinking has tended to distinguish carefully between diagnostic and therapeutic interventions, the meaning model suggests that diagnosis may in part also be treatment. One would hypothesize, then, that from among a group of patients with similar complaints, those given both a placebo and an understandable diagnostic label for their symptoms would have more relief than those given a placebo alone. This is important for group formation also: "We see how important it is that illness be given a legitimate name, that a sufferer have a mantle for his distress that society will accept" (Cassell 1976, p. 66).

Diagnoses, of course, have been designed by physicians to function within the explanatory system of scientific medicine, but with education of the public, most common diagnoses have become part of the explanatory system of the lay public. Thus, in most cases, the diagnosis will play a role in the patient's system formation, especially if the physician takes the time to explain the diagnosis and answer any questions about it. In most illness episodes, the disease is mild and self-limiting, and so knowing the correct diagnosis is likely to exert a positive placebo effect. Even where the prognosis for the disease is very poor, the patient's symptoms might improve once the diagnosis is transmitted to him; a grim certainty is often preferable to paralyzing doubt. In a few cases, such as cancer, where the diagnostic label has been embroidered in the public mind by somewhat unrealistic dread, imparting the diagnosis might exert a negative placebo effect. This explains the traditional reluctance of physicians to report truthfully such diagnoses to the patient; although the amount of actual damage that may be done is probably overestimated (Oken 1961; Pemberton 1971; cf. McIntosh 1976).

The ways in which diagnostic labeling suggests meaning to the patient need to be studied more fully. It is noteworthy, for example, that people on a waiting list at a psychiatric clinic showed a cure rate significantly above the spontaneous-remission rate for their neuroses before they had actually been seen for treatment (Sloane et al. 1975).[3] Thus, merely being accepted as a prospective patient by a psychiatric facility may count as sufficient diagnosis to lend enhanced meaning and symbolic coherence to the patient's subjective experience—all the more so because meaninglessness and lack of coherence are key features of the problem. Even though patients typically fear the label of mental illness, the label, once accepted, holds out promise that the condition can be understood and treated. For such patients, the waiting list itself apparently counts as part of the healing context. It would be worthwhile to see if such a phenomenon could be documented among patients on a waiting list to receive treatment for somatic complaints.[4]

Certain behaviors of patients, puzzling at present, become more understandable when the symbolic function of the healing context is taken into account. There is a growing body of medical literature on why patients often fail to comply with the regimen of prescribed treatment. Since most of the literature assumes that the patient comes to the physician to receive the prescription for the regimen, failure to comply constitutes irrational behavior. If, on the contrary, patients come to physicians largely to confer meaning on the illness experience, this function has been completed once the physician pronounces a diagnosis and reinforces it by writing a prescription; the actual taking of the drug may be less important (Pellegrino 1976*b*). Research on patient compliance would be more insightful if it took the symbolic functions of the physician-patient encounter into account more explicitly in the experimental design.

Other situations besides the healing context can markedly change one's sense of meaning, and the meaning model suggests that these situations also have the power to influence physical symptoms. A growing body of research has correlated the quantity of "life change," such as changes in residence and jobs, retirement, marriage, and death of a family member, with the likelihood of developing an organic disease in the months following (Rahe et al. 1964; Holmes and Rahe 1967; Rabkin and Struening 1976). An important feature of such findings is that the quantity of change is a stronger predictive indicator than whether the change is commonly viewed in positive or negative terms (e.g., marriage and divorce affect health equally).

Another focus for research might be comparisons between the placebo effect and related phenomena. An interesting parallel might be drawn, for example, between the placebo effect and psychotherapy. Jerome Frank, in his very perceptive *Persuasion and Healing* (1974), compares the various contemporary schools of psychotherapy with one another, as well as psychotherapy with the placebo effect, faith healing, shamanistic healing rituals, and religious revivalism. He concludes that there are important shared elements among the psychotherapeutic schools, and that in terms of explaining their general levels of efficacy, their similarities are more important than their differences. Frank lists four features as common to all schools of psychotherapy: (1) the patient's confidence in the therapist's ability and desire to help, (2) a socially sanctioned healing locale, especially one in which the patient can behave in ways that would not be acceptable elsewhere, (3) a "myth" or basic conceptual paradigm to explain the patient's symptoms in broad terms, and (4) a task to perform that involves the patient actively and which, by giving initially successful results, counteracts the demoralization that most patients seeking therapy have experienced in life (pp. 325–30).

It is immediately apparent that these are precisely the factors that might be expected to enhance system formation and group formation in the meaning model—that is, the factors most responsible for success in psychotherapy might be the same factors responsible for the placebo effect.[5] To say this is certainly not to denigrate psychotherapy in any way. Chapter 1 provides ample evidence of the great power of the placebo effect, and anything that can claim for itself even part of this power deserves recognition as an effective therapeutic modality. One might view psychotherapy, in this regard, as a highly organized way of bringing the placebo effect to bear on a special class of patients who otherwise would be very resistant to it (except as an immediate and limited response to very specific symptoms).

One additional point of interest in Frank's list of common factors is the fourth factor's emphasis on the importance of having the patient acquire a sense of mastery or control. The meaning model might be said to include mastery and control by implication, since one of the primary reasons for understanding events is to be able to control them. But perhaps mastery and control are important enough concepts to be included explicitly as part of the model. We saw in §6.5 that techniques that increase the patient's sense of control over the illness offer attractive alternatives to deceptive placebo use (Egbert et al. 1964; Cassell 1976); one patient has described how being made to feel like a partner in the therapeutic enterprise represented a turning point in his illness (Cousins 1976).

According to the capacity theory, to have a mind is to confer meaning on the world through the use of symbols, and to use symbols is to have purposes and to engage in responsible beavior (§5.1). We can see, then, how intimately the concepts of meaning, mastery, and personhood are interconnected. One high priority for the field of philosophy of medicine ought to be the exploration of the impact of illness on the human person in light of these concepts. Cassell, for example (1976, pp. 38–45), suggests that in a very fundamental way, illness restricts one's capacity for rational behavior. To what extent is this true, and to what extent does this influence how we ought to treat the sick? For example, if Cassell's thesis is true to a significant degree, it would not be possible to take seriously any informed consent obtained from a patient who is ill at the time. In this area, empirical issues are closely bound up with philosophical ones; behavioral scientists might engage in a more detailed analysis of how patients move into and out of the sick role and how their subjective sense of meaning and control is altered accordingly (Siegler and Osmond 1973).[6]

The discussion of mastery and control suggests a modification of Adler and Hammett's original model which may serve to guide placebo research, as the examples in this section have shown. Although Adler and Hammett (1973, p. 597) stated their two elements were the "necessary and sufficient" conditions for the placebo effect, this is certainly not self-evident. Other important conditions may well be discovered in future study, and so the original language ought to be abandoned. The revised meaning model might read as follows:

> The placebo effect is most likely to occur when the following conditions are optimally met:
>
> 1. The patient is provided with an explanation for his illness which is consistent with his preexisting view of the world.
> 2. A group of individuals assuming socially sanctioned caring roles is available to provide emotional support for the patient.
> 3. The healing intervention leads to the patient's acquiring a sense of mastery and control over the illness.

While so far we have been focusing primarily on the resear implications of this model, there are, as well, obvious in plications to be considered in more detail.

7.2 THERAPEUTIC IMPLICATIONS
OF THE MEANING MODEL

While awaiting the results of research, the practicing physician can still draw guidance from the meaning model. Chapter 6 listed strong arguments against routine use of placebos in therapy, but the meaning model suggests a number of strategies for eliciting the placebo effect through nondeceptive means.

We have noted periodically that both positive and negative placebo effects may be observed. Even before looking for ways to elicit a positive placebo effect, the physician might be alert for ways to avoid a negative one. In general, a negative effect will result from unconscious neglect or undermining of the conditions of the meaning model. For example, a cold and distant physician may fail to provide sufficient emotional support and hence may interfere with formation of the caring group.

It would appear that a first step toward avoiding negative placebo effects, then, is to promote a greater understanding of the placebo response and to call to the attention of the practitioner the elements that we have included in the meaning model. (As a rule, those physicians who have been recognized by peers and patients for their humane and sympathetic approach have already incorporated into their therapeutic armamentarium all of the elements of the meaning model, whether or not they have ever received formal instruction on those points; so the meaning model is often taught implicitly by example even when it has been explicitly unrecognized.) In particular, further education on placebos could overturn several myths, still prevalent among practitioners, which data from chapter 1 have already shown to be false.

MYTH 1. If a patient responds to placebos, his symptom

is either feigned or imaginary; hence the placebo can be used in the differential diagnosis of "organic" as opposed to "psychogenic" disorders. (Placebos affect objectively measurable physiological processes, not just subjective reports; see case 2, above, for one example of placebo efficacy in a clearly "organic" condition.)[7]

MYTH 2. Placebos can relieve only pain or anxiety. (Placebos can influence virtually any condition or symptom upon which they have been tested in controlled trials.)

MYTH 3. Placebos, whether they help or not, at least are harmless. (Placebos can produce side effects and addiction like pharmacologically active drugs, and also help reinforce habitual drug-taking as a response to illness.)

MYTH 4. Only neurotic personality types respond to placebos. (There is no "placebo personality type," and very likely anyone might respond to placebos under the right conditions.)

Once such myths about the placebo effect are exorcised from medical practice, positive guidance can be gained from further attention to the elements of the meaning model. For example, the element of formation of the caring group should alert the physician to the importance of involving the family and other care givers in his team approach to the care of the patient. He ought to reinforce appropriate displays of caring and to be alert for dysfunctional patterns of interpersonal relations that might either deprive the patient of needed support or else continue the sick role beyond its proper limits. Recently, in the fields of psychiatry, social work, and family practice, much has been learned about the patterns of family interactions in health and disease, and several new techniques to aid distressed families have emerged (Kaplan et al. 1973; Worby and Babineau 1974; Worby and Gerard 1978).

Group formation, bypassing the family, may sometimes involve instead of one of the increasingly popular lay self-help groups. Organizations such as Weight Watchers and

Alcoholics Anonymous have achieved impressive records in dealing with chronic health-behavior problems that defy medical management. Where successful, such organizations may be seen to employ all three elements of the meaning model. In addition to the introduction of the individual to a group of people who care about his welfare, the group provides an appealing explanation of the underlying problem which emphasizes its treatable aspects, and the "we licked it, you can too" litany instills a sense of mastery and control. The skillful practitioner will be aware of these self-help groups and will direct his patients to them under the appropriate circumstances.

In §6.5 we reviewed several specific clinical examples of another element of the meaning model: the sense of mastery and control over the illness, illustrated, notably, in the Egbert (1964) study on reduction of postoperative pain. Regarding mastery, the clinician often has to walk a fine line and be very sensitive to the personal capabilities and psychological resources of each patient. Ideally, in encouraging specific strategies to demonstrate control over symptoms, the physician will begin with modest goals that are well within the patient's capacity. If the physician stresses the concept of control over symptoms and the patient subsequently experiences a worsening of symptoms, the therapeutic course suffers a three-pronged setback: the patient feels guilty for having failed to exercise the control that the physician seemed to expect, the patient fears future rejection by the physician because of this perceived failure, and the failure further cements the idea that control ultimately rests with the disease and not with the patient.

Such setbacks are most likely to occur when the physician goes out on a limb and delivers some sort of evangelical peptalk to the patient. This approach, while appearing to emphasize patient control, actually reinforces physician control, since it is the physician who dictates the proper course of action to the patient. In general, for a placebo effect to occur it is not necessary for the patient to feel himself in control; it is sufficient for him to feel that someone, such as the healer, has mastery over the disease. The physician-control approach is psychologically satisfying to the physician and probably serves the patient well in acute illnesses where faithful adherence to a specified therapeutic regimen offers the best chance for cure. But in chronic illnesses the patient must eventually become his own doctor and must himself manage to integrate continued care of his condition into his overall life plan. Here over-dependence upon the physician is most likely to be counter-productive.

The experienced physician is aware of many possible techniques for control of symptoms and can usefully recommend the appropriate techniques to the patient. But instead of recommending or dictating, he may ask the patient what techniques he has discovered for himself that most effectively mitigate symptoms. If the patient has discovered some techniques on his own, the physician may praise him for his resourcefulness and suggest their continued use. If the patient has never thought in terms of his own ability to control symptoms, the physician may suggest that he experiment with some new techniques and report on the results at the next visit. This approach, emphasizing the responsibility of the patient in dealing with chronic symptoms, contrasts markedly with the approach of giving a sugar pill. The latter approach, as Cabot noted, gives the message that the all-powerful physician can offer immediate relief through drugs, and that failure to accomplish this represents a failure of the medical art. The former approach gives the message that symptoms are indeed controllable, but often through a variety of nonpharmacological and commonplace techniques, usually involving a certain amount of trial and error before relief appears.

The final element of the meaning model calls attention to the patient's own explanation for illness. Despite a growing literature on patient education and physician-patient communication (Freemon et al. 1971; Rosenstock 1975; Sackett 1978), the emphasis in medical thinking has been on transmitting the approved medical-scientific explanation to the patient, instead of eliciting from the patient whatever explanatory model he may already have devised or learned within his own sociocultural environment. In anthropological studies of healing practices in primitive cultures, the disparity between the culturally accepted explanation for the disease and the Western-scientific explanation is striking. It has been realized only recently that the encounter between a physician and a middle-class, educated patient in the United States differs in this regard only in degree, and not in kind, from the encounter between the Western physician and the primitive tribesman. In both cases the patient's own, unstated explanatory model is likely to differ from the physician's model, even if the differences are subtle. Failure to be aware of these differences can, at worst, impede cure, and at best will deprive the physician of a powerful tool for eliciting the placebo effect.

Kleinman, Eisenberg and Good (1978) have suggested that a ''clinical social science'' should be understood as a study of the means for eliciting from the patient his own explantory model, so that, if necessary, crucial disparities between the patient's and the physician's models can be dealt with explicitly. They recommend that the following questions be made a part of every therapeutic encounter between doctor and patient: What do you think caused your problem? Why do you think it started when it did? How does your sickness produce its symptoms? How severe is it? How long will it last? What treatment is most appropriate?

The first impulse of the physician after uncovering a divergent explanatory model in the patient is to try to ''correct'' the explanation to suit scientific views. In some cases, however, especially in cases with hypochondriacal components or wherever the patient has a strong psychological stake in clinging to his existing explanation, the physician may draw out a more powerful placebo effect if he is able to work within the patient's explanatory system (Drossman 1978; Groves 1978).

CASE 3. A middle-aged widow was assigned to my practice and came to the office or called with a multitude of nonspecific complaints for which tests revealed no underlying bodily pathology. I attempted to explain to her that emotional stress often results in bodily symptoms, and I tried to help her instead to verbalize these stresses. She responded to this by arguing that she could see no connection between particular stressful situations and her symptoms, and delighted in describing symptoms that had occurred on days when she was feeling happy and at ease emotionally. During this period her visits and phone calls increased in frequency. Finally I dropped all discussion of emotions and began to focus on her symptoms, sympathizing with her plight and complimenting her on her ability to lead a somewhat normal life despite such aggravating illnesses. After several visits her phone calls and unscheduled office calls decreased markedly, and at her regular visits she reported less interference in her daily activities due to symptoms. She also gradually became more willing to discuss her emotional reactions to specific stresses, and her doses of several medications were tapered successfully.

According to my "enlightened" explanatory model, physicians ought to respond to both bodily and emotional distress, but they ought to label precisely the nature of the distress and to apply specific remedies in accordance with the label. According to the patient's explanatory model, physicians are supposed to focus on bodily complaints. My appearing to belittle her symptoms seemed to her to threaten a rejection, as the symptoms, by her model, were her only legitimate ticket of entry into the emotionally satisfying doctor-patient relationship; her only possible response to ward off such a rejection was to escalate the severity of her symptoms.

Occasionally a divergent explanatory model may not only inhibit therapy but may indeed cause illness.

CASE 4. Workers in an English ceramics factory complained of the recent onset of skin rashes and attributed these to the materials used in the plant. Extensive dermatologic testing failed to reveal sensitivity in any of the workers to substances found in the factory. The first woman to complain of symptoms was found to have an unrelated skin problem, and she had described her symptoms along with her hypothesis as to their origin to her coworkers in vivid terms. When the other workers were told of the negative results of the skin tests and that nervousness over their fellow worker's symptoms was the most likely cause for their complaints, they expressed relief and the epidemic of rashes immediately ceased (Maguire 1978).

Why have scientifically trained physicians been so reluctant to ask about, and then to work with, the explanatory models of their patients? It has been exasperatingly difficult to banish from the medical mentality the false dichotomy between the stereotyped scientific clinician, cold, aloof, and "professional" while superbly skilled in the latest rational therapy, and the stereotyped horse-and-buggy doctor of old—friendly, supportive, and beloved by his patients, yet totally helpless in the realm of scientific diagnosis and therapy. Carefully reasoned assaults on this false dichotomy, emphasizing that medicine requires both scientific and humanistic skills (Pelligrino 1974; Reiser 1978), have not changed the basic reality that the most severe intraprofessional penalties are for lack of scientific skills, rather than lack of humanistic and interpersonal skills. Promulgation of the meaning model might be one small additional contribution to banishing this dichotomy, since the growing body of research on the workings of the importance of the placebo effect demonstrates that the practitioner who holds interpersonal and humanistic skills in disdain is *therefore* an unscientific practitioner.

Obviously, many more implications of the meaning model for both research and therapeutics could be developed. For the purposes of this investigation, however, we ought not lose sight of the reflective equilibrium strategy that has been the overall plan. The implications listed so far are sufficient to allow us to turn once more to that plan and to assess, in a brief conclusion, how fully it has been carried out in the preceding pages.

Conclusion

The implications for research and therapy cited in the previous chapter support the value of our investigation of the placebo effect from a medical standpoint. As an exercise in philosophy of medicine, however, the investigation must also be judged according to its philosophical implications. It will not do to view philosophy of medicine in a patronizing way as an "applied" philosophy, in which accepted philosophical truths are used to illuminate medical questions. Since medicine to some degree constitutes a unique way of looking at the world—a way that involves the empirical, metaphysical, and normative realms in a complex interaction—any serious philosophical investigation in medicine ought to extend, or call into question, some of our existing philosophical theories and conclusions. Returning briefly to the reflective equilibrium strategy laid out in the introduction, I will now focus on one significant philosophical implication of the theory of the person. While a full development of this implication cannot be included here, and would in fact probably require another book of this length, a brief sketch may nevertheless be instructive.

Recall that we originally set out in search of (1) an empirical-conceptual account of the placebo effect that would clarify its nature and its boundaries, (2) a theory of the mind-body relation consistent with what we know about placebos, and (3) an ethical position on the use of placebos in therapy.

We desired that each of these three corners of the triangle (*a*) satisfactorily address the problems of the placebo effect, (*b*) contribute to our understanding of the other corners in turn, and (*c*) agree with or extend our existing considered judgments in these domains, including considered judgments unrelated to the placebo effect.

The empirical-conceptual corner evolved by reviewing the empirical data on placebos, subjecting it to critical analysis, and, finally, formulating a definition of *placebo effect* (§2.3). The mind-body corner took the form of the capacity theory of the person, which provided a symbolic-cultural dimension missing from more traditional philosophies of mind. And the normative corner essentially restated the accepted ethical arguments against deception, amplifying them in the placebo case by showing how unexplored alternatives might replace deceptive placebo practices.

Furthermore, each corner was found to agree for the most part with representative considered judgments. The formal definition essentially arose directly from considered judgments arrived at by looking at illustrative examples of the placebo effect and related phenomena. The capacity theory of person was found to give illuminating answers to many puzzling issues in philosophy of mind, including disembodied minds, psychophysical causality, and self-consciousness. And the ethical analysis provided answers in the placebo case that are fully consistent with both deontological and utilitarian modes of reasoning.

Finally, each corner of the triangle was supposed to shed light on the two other corners. The two most striking examples both arose from the formal definition:

First, the definition gave prominent attention to the belief of the subject that he is within a (culturally designated) healing context. Thus, mind-body views unable to give full accounts either of belief states or of the cultural dimensions of mental life, were found to be less satisfactory than the capacity theory of the person.

Second, *placebo effect* was defined independently from *placebo*. The suggestion that a placebo is not necessary to elicit the positive features of the placebo effect raised the question of whether alternatives to the deceptive use of placebos are possible. This hypothesis, mostly ignored in previous ethical discussions, has given rise to potential innovations in the empirical realm (see §7.1).

We have thus seen at least in outline form a conceptual-metaphysical, a conceptual-normative, and a normative-metaphysical side to our triangle. Of course, each instance of mutual illumination works both ways—if our formal definition gives us important hints to resolving ethical problems, then this fact provides further support for the formal definition itself. Finally, our ability to fill in the components of the triangle justifies our choice of the reflective equilibrium strategy in the first place, and recommends this strategy as we undertake the philosophical analysis of other problems that medicine may present.

Having come this far, what material have we acquired that is suitable for further philosophical reflection? The most obvious loose ends concern the capacity theory of the person. The objectives of the present investigation require no more than a demonstration that the capacity theory provides answers to mind-body puzzles as satisfactory as those of competing theories, with gaps and weaknesses that are no more glaring. It would be a much more extensive task to defend the capacity-theory account of, say, psychophysical causality against possible objections, to say nothing of shoring up other weak points in the theory itself. This task, while of great importance, would take one rather far afield from the medical context. I would like to propose instead a line of inquiry which focuses on the metaphysical-normative side of our triangle and thus has potential for shedding light indirectly on important features of the capacity theory.

The notion of *person* developed in the course of reviewing alternative mind-body theories has ethical as well as metaphysical import. Current thinking in medical ethics has emphasized that our concern, instead of being for life in the abstract (Clouser 1973), is more properly directed at the life of persons, a class not necessarily coextensive with the class of human beings (Engelhardt 1975*b*). The sense of *person* indicated in this ethical context is that of a being who can properly be said to be the subject of rights and interests. If certain humans, perhaps fetuses or the irreversibly comatose, turn out on analysis not to be persons in this sense, they cannot be said to have the right to life that persons have by virtue of being persons, and their deaths might be permissible if other, over-riding moral values were thereby served (e.g., Tooley 1972; Feinberg 1976). In general, arguments on this point proceed on the basis of capacities that human beings typically have and that these special classes of humans lack—capacities which (it is argued) are so central to our functioning as human brings that a member of the species *homo sapiens* lacking these capacities is as different from us, morally speaking, as a dog or a horse.

According to the capacity theory of the person, the capacity that separates humans from other animals, as far as mental life is concerned, is the capacity to use symbols in such a way that the symbols acquire meaning through that use. How is this mind capacity related to the capacities by virtue of which a being can be said to be the subject of rights and interests? In a full exploration of the relationship, the two notions *person-as-user-of-symbols* and *person-as-bearer-of-rights* might each shed new light on the other.[1]

One way of approaching the relationship among the capacities is Feinberg's (1976) suggestion that to be a being to whom rights can meaningfully be predicated (as opposed to, say, a rock, to which the assignment of rights would be absurd), one must necessarily be a bearer of interests. And to have interests, a being must have the capacities we have been discussing as mind capacities: "however interests are ultimately to be analyzed, they must be compounded somehow out of wants and purposes, both of which in turn presuppose something like expectation, belief, and cognitive awareness'' (Feinberg 1976, p. 349). Put another way, a being that can have interests of its own is a being for which something can be a good *for its own sake* (in Kantian language, being an end and not a means only). And, in order for there to be an "own sake" at all, there must be self-consciousness, in the sense that a symbol user gives meaning to the symbols *through his own use* of them. Furthermore, we have already argued that to be a symbol user in this sense is necessarily to have purposes and goals (§5.1).

A coordinated inquiry into the concept of *person* from both the metaphysical and normative points of view has important implications for medicine. In chapter 2 we alluded to the placebo effect as an anomaly within the presently accepted medical paradigm. An important feature of anomalies is that once they become the focus of research, they can lead to the overthrow or at least the modification of the existing paradigm.

To many critics of modern medicine, this existing medical paradigm is characterized by failure to embrace the whole person. Instead the individual has been reduced to a seat for pathology or to a physiological mechanism.[2] On this account, medicine has engaged in a dissection of the person similar to the outrage that is said to have been committed by the Cartesian dualist tradition in philosophy of mind.

But if a modified paradigm is to be offered to replace the existing one, if *whole person* is to be more than a slogan, then some comprehensive philosophy of the person is required (Engelhardt 1975*b*).[3] This view of the person must be conceptually sound, consistent with the best empirical knowledge, and suggestive of new lines of empirical inquiry. It must embrace the person as a biological organism, as the subject of rights and interests and as the bearer of duties, as a subject of conscious self-awareness, and as a dweller within society and culture. Our discussion of the placebo effect has touched upon all these features. Properly developed, a study of the placebo effect can do much to highlight the centrality of the whole person both to philosophy of medicine and to medical practice.

Notes

1. The model for philosophical inquiry that I am employing is an expansion of Rawls's "reflective equilibrium" for determining principles of justice most compatible with our basic moral judgments (1971, pp. 18–22). Rawls in turn cites Nelson Goodman on the justification of principles of scientific inference, suggesting that some related concept of "best overall fit" may be applicable within philosophy of science as well. I take Lakatos's (1970) description of "research programmes" in science to involve a similar equilibrium model; scientists have characterized this as a cybernetic or a negative-feedback model, as contrasted to the hypothetico-deductive model (Medawar 1967, p. 154).

2. The "equilibrium" must involve changes in both directions, since if our existing considered judgments were never altered to fit attractive general principles, the system would offer little opportunity for growth. We are rather looking for general principles which, if they do not match our most basic considered judgments, "extend them in an acceptable way" (Rawls 1971, p. 19).

3. On the scope of this new subdiscipline see Pellegrino (1976a). An illuminating debate on the possibility and the nature of a philosophy of medicine is found in Engelhardt and Spicker (1975, pp. 211–34).

4. This preconception of philosophy is neither new nor original. On the importance of a subjective sense of satisfac-

tion, and of taking moral as well as conceptual elements into account when seeking *fit,* see James (1927, pp. 146–48).

5. Throughout this book I will be using the undesirable masculine noun and pronoun forms for purposes of brevity, and also in order to reserve the term *person* to designate the particular philosophical stance described in chapters 4 and 5.

CHAPTER ONE

1. In a double-blind trial, neither investigator nor experimental subject knows whether the subject is in the control or the experimental group. Thus if the experimental group is to receive a drug or other treatment, the control group must get a dummy treatment outwardly resembling the experimental one but lacking the ingredient under study.

2. The use of the word *mimic* might unintentionally suggest that the placebo effect is somehow less real than the pharmacologic effect of drugs. The problem of using neutral language in describing the placebo effect, so as not unwittingly to beg the interesting questions, must be kept in mind.

3. These findings should put a lie to the myth, still prevalent among physicians, that if a patient responds to placebo his symptoms must be either imaginary or feigned and that a placebo can be used in the differential diagnosis of psychic symptoms from "organic" ones.

4. For more on this waiting-list study see chapter 7, especially note 3.

5. It would have been interesting to employ as part of this study a true placebo or "dummy" biofeedback (i.e., the biofeedback signal given to the subject randomly, instead of only when the subject was exhibiting alpha rhythm); unfortunately this was not done. This omission casts even more doubt on whether the index formulated by the investigators was measuring a "placebo" response.

6. This reluctance may stem from the desire to try simpler hypotheses with more readily measurable variables, and also from the trend in psychosomatic research in the 1940s and 1950s to define "personality types" associated with specific diseases. One might speculate that had watchmakers conducted the first experiments on hypnosis, they would have

tried to correlate the trance state with the type of watch being swung before the subjects' eyes, and would have been chagrined when such a correlation failed to appear.

7. To my knowledge this paper by Byerly is the only attempt to date to approach the placebo effect from the philosophical standpoint.

8. Beecher's two-stage pain theory derived from studies of narcotics in treating war wounds; soldiers given morphine claimed that they still felt pain but were no longer bothered by it. Beecher concluded that pain consists of two phases, the sensation and the emotional reaction to it. I cannot fully evaluate the tenability of this view here; but see the comments on "Pain and Suffering" by Jerome Shaffer in Spicker and Englehardt (1976, pp. 221–33).

9. It could, of course, be argued that not one mechanism but several are responsible for the placebo effect. Beecher (1955) took the reproducibility of placebo response rates from study to study (an average of 35.2 percent, with a standard deviation of 2.2 percent, in fifteen studies covering a variety of symptoms) as evidence supporting a single mechanism.

10. Only after completing this portion of the manuscript did I learn of "Placebo: An Annotated Bibliography" by J. L. Turner, R. Gallimore, and C. Fox (Neuropsychiatric Institute, UCLA, mimeographed). This collection of 919 references should prove a valuable guide for future reviewers.

CHAPTER TWO

1. *Paradigm* may refer either to the body of shared beliefs of a scientific community, or specifically to puzzle-solving examples of that community which have the most direct impact on research design (Kuhn 1970, pp. 174–91). The sense in which I use the term here approximates the former, referring especially to the elements of heuristic models (e.g., of disease causation) and values (e.g., what counts as a "good" explanation). But the latter sense cannot be completely separated from this use—the place of Koch's postulates in contemporary medical science shows how values, heuristic models, and puzzle-solving examples are mutually bound together.

2. Respect for the body's self-healing potential is justified by

such classic treatments as Cannon's (1963). Whether modern medical practices are so clearly superior to those of the past, however, is cogently called into question by Powles (1973).

3. Recall Shapiro's (1968) suggestion that the placebo effect can be either positive or negative; for simplicity's sake the case illustrations will deal only with positive placebo effects except where noted.

4. I will not, of course, attempt to defend the ethics of such an experiment, were it to be done deliberately.

5. The objection raised in case 2 above does not apply here. "Practically indistinguishable" does not mean empirically undetectable in principle; it merely challenges the ingenuity of the investigator for controlling for subtle variables.

6. I am indebted to David S. Sobel for this example.

7. For discussion of the sick role from the sociological perspective see Parsons (1951), Parsons (1961), Siegler and Osmond (1973), and Friedson (1970, pp. 205–43).

8. Hence, treatment problems arise for Western medicine when the patient adheres to folk medical beliefs of his own subculture not understood by his physicians (Snow 1974).

9. Psychological risk factors in open heart surgery are currently being studied by Dr. Sumer Verma (personal communication).

10. Eventually the similarities among the different classes of phenomena may turn out to be so striking that *placebo effect* will be dropped altogether in favor of a more general term such as *autosuggestion*. Still, the term *placebo* would remain in use to designate a dummy medication or treatment.

11. I am indebted to Martin Benjamin for this example.

12. The absurdity here is similar to that in a story Abraham Lincoln liked to tell, about an Irishman who had taken an abstinence pledge and was forced to order lemonade at a bar on a hot day; he finally leaned confidentially toward the barkeeper and asked, "Couldn't you put a wee drop o' the creetur into it unbeknownst to me?" (Sandburg 1939, vol. 1, p. 572, vol. 4, p. 158).

13. In the nonblind placebo trial (Park and Covi 1965), several of the patients responding positively had initially ex-

pressed doubts that placebos would work. If placebos can work in the face of doubt, they ought to work also in the weaker cases of nonbelief.

14. See, however, the formal definitions and discussion in §2.3, below, on why a placebo need not be present for the placebo effect to be said to occur.

15. Modell elsewhere seems aware of this problem when he states that the placebo effect invariably accompanies every *prescription* of a drug (1955, p. 54).

16. *Who* believes this is deliberately left vague; it might be the person with C, the person administering T, or some third party as outside observer. The importance of specifying which of these hold for a specific case is illustrated by the witch doctor example in §2.1 above.

17. I am suggesting here that the notion of *therapy* is connected very intimately with that of *disease,* a point I cannot argue for here. Unfortunately recent philosophical inquiries into the concepts of *health* and *disease* have almost totally neglected this point.

18. Since what counts as a healing context depends on the culture of the individual, inclusion of this term in the definition means that the placebo effect is inherently culture-dependent (Riley 1976).

19. Note that I may not be known specifically. In the sugar-pill case, the cause of the symptom change is assumed not to be the chemical content of the pill, and because no other medication is known to have been used, *some* other element of the total episode is assumed to be responsible.

CHAPTER THREE

1. See, for example, Engelhardt's analysis of the research-connected motivations that led the nineteenth-century neurologist John Hughlings Jackson to adopt the doctrine of parallelism (Engelhardt 1975*a*).

2. An exception is the approach taken by the philosopher-physician Tristram Engelhardt. His more sophisticated theory, in the Kantian-Hegelian tradition, takes mind and body to be two separate domains of significance, such that attempts to

relate them causally constitute category mistakes. On matters such as psychosomatic medicine and the placebo effect, his views seem to be a type of epiphenomenalism; but this may be my misreading of his position (Engelhardt 1973).

3. That mind-body theories give us vague accounts of the placebo effect should not by itself count against them; we do not want philosophical theories to fill in details that can properly be provided only by further empirical research.

4. In its organization, this section roughly follows Shaffer (1967). For an overview of significant contemporary positions on mind-body within the Anglo-American tradition, see Chappell (1962), Shaffer (1965).

5. For the original statement of this position see Descartes (1927, pp. 145–65); Spicker (1970, pp. 3–23) provides a summary of the problems that it raises.

6. The view that all medical thinking is necessarily causal derives from our own dominant paradigm. The entire, complex system of ancient Chinese medicine was essentially noncausal (Porkert 1979). In the paradigm dominant in eighteenth-century Europe, recognition of disease was based on the concept of a "motionless, simultaneous picture" (Foucault 1975, pp. 3–16, 188–89).

7. Such behavior need not be readily observable in practice for the behaviorist to make his metaphysical case. For example, some have attempted to analyze thought in terms of subvocal laryngeal contractions.

8. But see §5.2 below for a refinement of Gasking's position, suggesting that there is no one "root sense" of causation.

9. I owe my understanding of this refinement of Wiggins's analysis to an unpublished paper by Martin Benjamin.

10. James Cornman, "The Identity of Mind and Body," in Borst (1970, pp. 123–29) argues for "cross-category" identity, such as "the temperature of the gas is identical to the mean kinetic energy of its molecules." But if the identity is truly cross-category, there can be no common sortal concept, and the identity statement is incoherent. Indeed, in Cornman's example, "identical to" seems strained at best; "directly proportional to" is much more natural.

CHAPTER FOUR

1. Representative papers on the *disappearance form* are Richard Rorty, "Mind-Brain Identity, Privacy, and Categories," and Paul Feyerabend, "Materialism and the Mind-Body Problem" (Borst 1970, pp. 187–213, 142–56).

2. I am indebted to Joseph Hanna for pointing out to me the possibility of such an account.

3. Obviously the radical behaviorist's use of mentalistic terms with radically modified meanings makes argument in this area especially difficult; and to some extent, as we will show below, the plausibility of the behaviorist's position depends on this ambiguity. This sort of language problem is a general feature of cross-paradigm debates in science (Kuhn 1970, pp. 198–204).

4. Further justification for combining the two theories is that radical behaviorism seems especially strong in accounting for intentional states, whereas the disappearance form is most credible in dealing with sensations.

5. To weaken this example, the materialist might suggest that it does not make us doubt the existence of a one-to-one or a many-to-one correspondence; it merely makes us doubt our ability to articulate it in ordinary language.

6. Fodor here does not deny that functional explanations play a role within neurophysiology itself; but where the behavior of human beings is concerned, all neurophysiological explanation, whatever its internal form, is mechanistic.

7. This argument applies to the disappearance form, but—to the extent that it includes functional explanations of behavior—not to Skinner's radical behaviorism.

8. Platt's assertion is supported by a trend in philosophy of science—namely, the view that observation is inherently theory-laden—which emphasizes the scientist as an active participant in what he studies (e.g., Hanson 1958).

9. It will not do for the skeptic to claim he accepts the notion of *person,* but doubts whether the other bodies that he observes are persons. Persons, which are not mind-plus-body in the Cartesian sense, *can* be adequately known and identified through their bodies. To take this position, the skeptic ceases

to be merely an other-minds skeptic and becomes skeptical about the reality of the physical world.

CHAPTER FIVE

1. Grene sees her amplification of Kenny's account arising from the tradition of continental philosophers Helmuth Plessner and Maurice Merleau-Ponty and from the epistemology of Michael Polanyi. Since the Kenny-Grene account can stand on its own, I have not attempted to investigate these sources or other matters of historical background, but have concentrated on the theory itself.

2. This observation and what follows leave open the possibility that nonhumans, such as chimpanzees who have learned sign language, creatures from outer space, or highly sophisticated machines, could be persons. I accept this, but since our major concern is with humans, I will use *human* and *person* interchangeably. The arguments that follow also suggest that nonhuman persons would necessarily be tied to their bodies in a way analogous to humans.

3. Wittgenstein contrasted the idea of multiple resemblances, which "overlap and criss-cross" among members of a class, with the idea of one essential element as the common denominator among all members. "The strength of the thread does not reside in the fact that some one fibre runs through its whole length, but in the overlapping of many fibers" (1958, I, 67). See also Kenny (1973b, pp. 153–63).

4. Frankfurt (1971) argues that what distinguishes humans from other animals is the capacity to form second-order desires; if the Kenny-Grene account is correct, it would seem that being a symbol user in the proper sense is both necessary and sufficient for having second-order desires (a point which requires further exploration).

5. Specifically: "To have a mind is to have the capacity to acquire the ability to operate with symbols in such a way that it is one's own activity that makes them symbols and confers meaning on them" (Kenny 1973a, p. 47).

6. This failure to look for alternative types of causation is seen in the Cartesian interactionist view. If the body is viewed as a sort of mechanistic clockwork, it is assumed that the mind,

in order to affect the body causally, must be of the same category, i.e., substance. Thus mind ends up as a mysterious sort of nonmechanistic clockwork (i.e., mechanical but noncorporeal) (Ryle 1949, pp. 18–20).

7. Implicit in this statement is a distinction between *disease*, the explanatory model employed by the culturally designated healer, and *illness*, the subjective experience of the sick individual. For more on this distinction, see Kleinman (1973), Cassell (1976, pp. 47–83).

8. In other cases, such as the physical sciences, vehicle reductionism might be appropriate—e.g., "Magnetism is the alignment of molecules in certain metals." The reasons why vehicle reductionism is inappropriate for the mind parallel the reasons for rejecting eliminative materialism (§4.2). See also the discussion of reductionism in §5.4 below.

9. Strawson, who agrees with Penelhum on identity criteria, would still hold that a disembodied person would maintain his identity by virtue of having been a person (1958, pp. 341–42); presumably this person could have memories but no new experiences. Penelhum refutes even this, noting that the concept of memory is parasitic upon the concept of identity, not vice versa, so that we have no idea to whom to ascribe the purported memories of having been a person.

10. "In order to have this type of concept [of mental predicates] one must be both a self-ascriber and an other-ascriber of such predicates, and must see every other as a self-ascriber" (Strawson 1958, p. 346). Had Strawson defined *person* as a *self*-ascriber of mental predicates, rather than as an individual to which mental predicates may be ascribed, he would have avoided Frankfurt's criticisms (1971); see §4.3 above. I owe this observation to Martin Benjamin.

11. "We only say that someone speaks to himself if, in the ordinary sense of the word, he *can speak*" (Wittgenstein 1958, I, 344; cf. Ryle 1949, pp. 27, 200).

CHAPTER SIX

1. The material in this chapter represents a considerable expansion upon and revision of Brody (1975).

2. Secondary sources on the history of placebos are lacking.

Shapiro (1960) is a history of ineffectual remedies rather than a history of placebo use; Brodeur (1965) does not go beyond Shapiro; and McMahon (1975), tracing theories that could explain the placebo effect, does not document the use of placebos.

3. Significantly, Tuke in his five-page discussion of hope and expectation never uses the word *placebo*. This points out a major problem for anyone attempting a historical survey, as I have done, by searching indexes or tables of contents of medical works from various periods.

4. One interesting exception might be studies of the placebo effect itself, in which it might be necessary to conceal part of the experimental design—e.g., if one were trying to measure directly the extent to which the placebo effect depends on deception in various circumstances. The important issue of when deception can be justified in research is beyond the scope of this discussion; but see Soble (1978).

5. Here we are assuming proper diagnosis, selection of a remedy indicated by the patient's condition, and so on.

6. In §1.3 we cited one example of successful nondeceptive use of an inert pill (Park and Covi 1965), but I am reluctant to overgeneralize from this intriguing but limited study. Suffice it to say that as most commonly utilized by the majority of medical practitioners, placebo use involves deception.

7. This argument assumes the perpetuation of the Cabot-era relationship between the medical profession and the remainder of society and ignores current movements toward greater "consumer input" into health matters and better patient education (e.g., Rabkin 1973; Vickery and Fries 1976). Thus the chance of "being found out" is probably increasing steadily.

8. Here we are speaking of a positive placebo effect, recalling that our definition allows for both positive and negative placebo effects (see Shapiro 1968).

9. For a similar example of changing the "meaning" of an illness experience without the use of deception, see case 1 in chapter 7, below. Though Cassell does not use the term *placebo effect,* his strategy of teaching the patient greater control over bodily function seems similar in principle to Egbert's (Cassell 1976, pp. 154–62).

10. Even if nondeceptive strategies were somewhat less effective, as compared to placebo use, the gain from avoiding the negative consequences of deception could offset this in a utilitarian calculus.

11. Conceivably, overemphasis on self-control of symptoms and avoidance of medications and surgery could cause patients to delay seeking needed medical attention for serious conditions, but this potential negative consequence can be avoided by additional patient education (e.g., Vickery and Fries 1976).

12. This chapter was completed without the benefit of the excellent book by Sissela Bok, 1978. *Lying: Moral choice in public and private life*. New York: Pantheon. Bok's analysis of deception in chapter 2 and of placebos viewed as a type of white lie in chapter 5 provides a valuable expansion of several of the points raised above.

CHAPTER SEVEN

1. For references on the sick role see note 7, chapter 2.

2. This is not to suggest that emotional factors are not important. Frank, reviewing studies of faith healing at Lourdes, noted that visitors who are emotionally involved, either as believers or as skeptics, were more likely to have symptom relief than the indifferent ones (1974, pp. 71–72). Clearly both emotions and beliefs need to be studied in any comprehensive research into the placebo effect.

3. A problem with this interpretation of the study is that the subjects were interviewed by a psychiatric assessor to determine symptom severity prior to being placed on a waiting list; this "strictly evaluative" (from the authors' standpoint) intervention may have been perceived by the patients as therapy.

4. Primary-care and emergency physicians are often impressed by the frequency with which symptoms seem to abate as soon as the sufferer has made up his mind to seek medical care.

5. Frank himself denies that psychotherapy relies upon the placebo effect for its results, but this conclusion may arise from the relatively more narrow way in which he construes the placebo effect—skimming over the importance of belief sys-

tems and emphasizing emotional factors (1974, pp. 136–64).

6. Barnlund (1976) notes that factors complicating inter-personal communication are at their height in illness contexts and outlines research possibilities in the symbolic and communicative aspects of illness.

7. The raised-eyebrow quotation marks around "organic" are intended to call attention to the fact that this myth rests largely on an over-rigid dichotomy between mental and physical processes, which is both conceptually unsatisfactory and therapeutically misleading, as has been emphasized in previous chapters.

CONCLUSION

1. Kenny's language, "capacity to acquire the ability" (1973a, p. 47), might support the position that fetuses are persons in the full sense. I think, however, that one must distinguish between the *capacity* to acquire the ability to operate with symbols, and the *potential* to acquire the ability; fetuses seem to possess the latter but not the former. This needs, of course, to be defended at greater length.

2. Since the current concern with whole-patient medicine is sometimes termed *neohippocratic,* it is interesting that some of medicine's modern sins can be traced back to the concepts and practices of the ancient Hippocratics, who, "with their drive for rationalism and objectivity, were casting aside the use of the spoken word in medicine and were laying the basis for the modern physician who does not speak to his patients" (Cassell 1976, p. 56).

3. Indications of the need for a comprehensive view of the person have come also from fields outside philosophy—e.g., Fletcher (1972), Trosko (1975).

Bibliography

Adler, H. M., and Hammett, V. B. O. 1973. The doctor-patient relationship revisited: An analysis of the placebo effect. *Annals of Internal Medicine* 78:595–98.

Barnlund, D. C. 1976. The mystification of meaning: Doctor-patient encounters. *Journal of Medical Education* 51: 716–25.

Beecher, H. K. 1955. The powerful placebo. *Journal of the American Medical Association* 159:1602–6.

————. 1961. Surgery as placebo: A quantitative study of bias. *Journal of the American Medical Association* 176:1102–7.

Benjamin, M. 1976. Medical practice and the theory of action. Paper presented at the Conference on Philosophy, Law, and Medicine, 15–17 October 1976, Kalamazoo, Mich.

Benson, H., and Epstein, M. D. 1975. The placebo effect: A neglected asset in the care of patients. *Journal of the American Medical Association* 232:1225–27.

Blanton, W. B. 1931. *Medicine in Virginia in the eighteenth century*. Richmond: Garrett and Massie.

Bok, S. 1974. The ethics of giving placebos. *Scientific American*, November issue, pp. 17–23.

Bok, S. 1978. *Lying: Moral choice in public and private life*. New York: Pantheon.

Borst, C. V., ed. 1970. *The mind-brain identity theory*. New York: St. Martin's Press.

Boss, J. 1975. Physiology and psychology: Toward a practical philosophy. *Medical Hypotheses*, vol. 1.

Bottle of medicine, the. (Editorial.) 1952. *British Medical Journal* 1:149–50.

Bourne, H. R. 1971. The placebo—a poorly understood and neglected therapeutic agent. *Rational Drug Therapy*, November issue, pp. 1–6.

Brodeur, D. W. 1965. A short history of placebos. *Journal of the American Pharmaceutical Association* 5:642, 662.

Brody, H. 1975. Commentary: On placebos. *Hastings Center Report* 5 (April): 17–18.

————. 1976. *Ethical decisions in medicine.* Boston: Little, Brown and Co.

Byerly, H. 1976. Explaining and exploiting placebo effects. *Perspectives in Biology and Medicine* 19:423–36.

Cabot, R. C. 1909. *Social service and the art of healing.* New York: Moffat, Yard and Co.

Cannon, W. B. 1963. *The wisdom of the body.* New York: W. W. Norton and Co.

Cassell, E. J. 1976. *The healer's art: A new approach to the doctor-patient relationship.* Philadelphia: J. B. Lippincott Co.

Chappell, V. C., ed. 1962. *The philosophy of mind.* Englewood Cliffs, N.J.: Prentice-Hall.

Chisholm, R. M. 1957. *Perceiving.* Ithaca: Cornell University Press.

Clouser, K. D. 1973. 'The sanctity of life': An analysis of a concept. *Annals of Internal Medicine* 78:119–25.

Conferences on therapy: The use of placebos in therapy. 1976. *New York State Journal of Medicine* 46:1718–27.

Cousins, N. 1976. Anatomy of an illness (as perceived by the patient). *New England Journal of Medicine* 295:1458–63.

Descartes, R. 1927. *Selections,* ed. R. M. Eaton. New York: Charles Scribners Sons.

Drossman, D. A. 1978. The problem patient: Evaluation and care of medical patients with psychosocial disturbances. *Annals of Internal Medicine* 88:366–72.

Egbert, L. D.; Battit, G. E.; Welch, C. E.; and Bartlett, M. K. 1964. Reduction of postoperative pain by encouragement and instruction of patients. *New England Journal of Medicine* 270:825–27.

Engel, G. L. 1978. Psychologic stress, vasodepressor (vaso-vagal) syncope, and sudden death. *Annals of Internal Medicine* 89:403–12.

Englehardt, H. T., Jr. 1973. *Mind-body: A categorial relation.* The Hague: Martinus Nijhoff.

———. 1975*a*. John Hughlings Jackson and the mind-body relation. *Bulletin of the History of Medicine* 49:137–51.

———. 1975*b*. The patient as person: An empty phrase? *Texas Medicine* 71:57–63.

Engelhardt, H. T., Jr., and Spicker, S. F., eds. 1975. *Evaluation and explanation in the biomedical sciences.* Dordrecht, Holland: D. Reidel Publishing Co.

Evans, F. J. 1974. The power of a sugar pill. *Psychology Today,* April issue, pp. 55–61.

Fabrega, H., Jr. 1976. The function of medical-care systems: A logical analysis. *Perspectives in Biology and Medicine* 20:108–19.

Feinberg, J. 1970. *Doing and deserving: Essays in the theory of responsibility.* Princeton: Princeton University Press.

———. 1976. Is there a right to be born? In *Understanding moral philosophy,* ed. J. Rachels. Encino, Cal.: Dickenson.

Findley, T. 1953. The placebo and the physician. *Medical Clinics of North America* 37:1821–26.

Fletcher, J. 1972. Indicators of humanhood: A tentative profile of man. *Hastings Center Report* 2 (November): 1–3.

Fodor, J. A. 1965. Explanations in psychology. In *Philosophy in America,* ed. M. Black. Ithaca: Cornell University Press.

Forrer, G. R. 1964. Psychoanalytic theory of placebo. *Diseases of the Nervous System* 25:655–61.

Foucault, M. 1975. *The birth of the clinic: An archaeology of medical perception.* Translated by A. M. Sheridan Smith. New York: Vintage Books.

Frank, J. D. 1974. *Persuasion and healing.* New York: Schocken Books.

Frankfurt, H. G. 1971. Freedom of the will and the concept of a person. Journal of Philosophy 68:5–20.

Freedman, A. M.; Kaplan, H. I.; and Sadock, B. J. 1972. *Modern synopsis of comprehensive textbook of psychiatry.* Baltimore: Williams and Wilkins.

Freedman, N; Cutler, R.; Engelhardt, D. M.; and Margolis, R. 1967. On the modification of paranoid symptomatology. *Journal of Nervous and Mental Disease* 144:29–36.

Freemon, B.; Negrete, V. F.; Davis, M.; and Korsch, B. M. 1971. Gaps in doctor-patient communication: Doctor-patient interaction analysis. *Pediatric Research* 5:298–311.

Freund, P. A., ed. 1969. *Experimentation with human subjects.* New York: George Braziller.

Fried, C. 1974. *Medical experimentation: Personal integrity and social policy.* Amsterdam: North-Holland Publishers.

Friedson, E. 1970. *Professor of medicine.* New York: Harper and Row.

Fuchs, V. R. 1974. *Who shall live? Health, economics, and social choice.* New York: Basic Books.

Gartner, M. A., Jr. 1961. Selected personality differences between placebo reactors and nonreactors. *Journal of the American Osteopathic Association* 60:377–78.

Gasking, D. 1955. Causation and recipes. *Mind* 64:479–87.

Gliedman, L. H.; Gantt, W. H.; and Teitelbaum, H. A. 1957. Some implications of conditional reflex studies for placebo research. *American Journal of Psychiatry* 113:1103–7.

Goldberg, B. 1968. The correspondence hypothesis. *Philosophical Review* 77:438–54.

Graham, D. T. 1967. Health, disease, and the mind-body problem: Linguistic parallelism. *Psychosomatic Medicine* 29:52–71.

Grene, M. 1971. Reducibility: another side issue? In *Interpretations of life and mind,* ed. M. Grene. New York: Humanities Press.

———. 1976. To have a mind... *Journal of Medicine and Philosophy* 1:177–99.

Gross, S. W. 1887. *A practical treatise on impotence, sterility, and allied disorders of the male sexual organs.* 3d ed. Philadelphia: Lea Brothers and Co.

Groves, J. E. 1978. Taking care of the hateful patient. *New England Journal of Medicine* 298:883–87.

Hanson, N. R. 1958. *Patterns of discovery: An inquiry into the conceptual foundations of science.* Cambridge: Cambridge University Press.

Holmes, T. H., and Rahe, R. H. 1967. The social readjustment rating scale. *Journal of Psychosomatic Research* 11:213–18.

Honzak, R.; Horackova, E.; and Culik, A. 1972. Our experience with the effect of placebo in some functional and psychosomatic disorders. *Activitas Nervosa Superior (Prague)* 14:184–85.

Houston, W. R. 1938. The doctor himself as a therapeutic agent. *Annals of Internal Medicine* 11:1416–25.

James, W. 1896. *The will to believe and other essays in popular philosophy.* Reprint ed. New York: Longmans, Green and Co., 1927.

Jellinek, E. M. 1946. Clinical tests on comparative effectiveness of analgesic drugs. *Biometrics Bulletin* 2:87.

Kaplan, D. M.; Smith, A.; Grobstein, R.; and Fischman, S. E. 1973. Family mediation of stress. *Social Work* 18 (July): 60–69.

Kenny, A. J. P. 1973*a*. The origin of the soul. In A. J. P. Kenny, H. C. Longuet-Higgins, J. R. Lucas, and C. H. Waddington. *The development of mind.* Edinburgh: The University Press.

———. 1973*b*. *Wittgenstein.* Cambridge, Mass.: Harvard University Press.

———. 1976. *Will, freedom and power.* New York: Barnes and Noble.

Kiritz, S., and Moos, R. H. 1974. Physiological effects of social environments. *Psychosomatic Medicine* 36:96–114.

Kleinman, A. M. 1973. Medicine's symbolic reality. *Inquiry* 16:203–16.

Kleinman, A. M.; Eisenberg, L.; and Good, B. 1978. Culture, illness and care: Clinical lessons from anthropological and cross-cultural research. *Annals of Internal Medicine* 88:251–58.

Kleinman, A. M., and Sung, L. H. 1976. Why do indigenous healers successfully heal? Paper presented at a workshop, "The Healing Process," April 1976, Michigan State University, East Lansing.

Klopfer, B. 1957. Psychological variables in human cancer. *Journal of Projective Techniques* 21:331–40.

Kristein, M. M.; Arnold, C. B.; and Wynder, E. L. 1977.

Health economics and preventive care. *Science* 195:457–62.

Kuhn, T. S. 1970. *The structure of scientific revolutions.* Chicago: University of Chicago Press.

Kurland, A. A. 1960. Placebo effect. In *Drugs and behavior,* ed. L. Uhr and J. G. Millar. New York: Wiley.

Lakatos, I. 1970. Falsification and the methodology of scientific research programmes. In *Criticism and the growth of knowledge,* ed. I. Lakatos and A. Musgrave. New York: Cambridge University Press.

Lasagna, L.; Laties, V. G.; and Dohan, J. L. 1958. Further studies on the 'pharmacology' of placebo administration. *Journal of Clinical Investigation* 37:533–37.

Lasagna, L.; Mosteller, F.; von Felsinger, J. M.; and Beecher, H. K. 1954. A study of the placebo response. *American Journal of Medicine* 16:770–79.

Leslie, A. 1954. Ethics and the practice of placebo therapy. *American Journal of Medicine* 16:854–62.

Levine, J. D.; Gordon, N. C.; and Fields, H. L. 1978. The mechanism of placebo analgesia. *Lancet* 2:654–57.

Lipowski, Z. J. 1973. Affluence, information inputs and health. *Social Science and Medicine* 7:517–29.

McIntosh, J. 1976. Patients' awareness and desire for information about diagnosed but undisclosed malignant disease. *Lancet* 2:300–3.

McMahon, C. E. 1975. The 'placebo effect' in renaissance medicine. *Journal of the American Society of Psychosomatic Dentistry and Medicine* 22:3–9.

Maguire, A. 1978. Psychic possession among industrial workers. *Lancet* 1:376–78.

Malcolm, N. 1968. The conceivability of mechanism. *Philosophical Review* 77:45–72.

Mason, R. C.; Clark, G.; Reeves, R. B.; and Wagner, S. B. 1969. Acceptance and healing. *Journal of Religion and Health* 8:123–42.

Medawar, P. B. 1967. *The art of the soluble.* London: Methuen and Co.

Melzack, R., and Wall, P. D. 1965. Pain mechanisms: A new theory. *Science* 150:971–79.

Modell, W. 1955. *The relief of symptoms*. Philadelphia: W. B. Saunders and Co.

Moore, M. E., and Berk, S. N. 1976. Acupuncture for chronic shoulder pain: An experimental study with attention to the role of placebo and hypnotic susceptibility. *Annals of Internal Medicine* 84:381–84.

Morris, L. A., and O'Neal, E. C. 1974. Drug-name familiarity and the placebo effect. *Journal of Clinical Psychology* 30:280–82.

Muller, B. P. 1965. Personality of placebo reactors and non-reactors. *Diseases of the Nervous System* 26:58–61.

Nash, M. M., and Zimring, F. M. 1969. Prediction of reaction to placebo. *Journal of Abnormal Psychology* 74:568–73.

Oken, D. 1961. What to tell cancer patients: A study of medical attitudes. *Journal of the American Medical Association* 175:1120–28.

Osmond, H. 1974. Placebos and testing models. *Medical Counterpoint*, June–July issue, pp. 16 ff.

Park, L. C., and Covi, L. 1965. Nonblind placebo trial: An exploration of neurotic outpatients' responses to placebo when its inert content is disclosed. *Archives of General Psychiatry* 12:336–45.

Parsons, T. 1951. *The social system*. New York: Free Press.

————. 1961. Illness and the role of the physician: A sociological perspective. In *Personality in nature, society, and culture*, ed. C. Kluckholn, H. A. Murray, and D. M. Schneider. New York: Alfred A. Knopf.

Pellegrino, E. D. 1974. Educating the humanist physician: An ancient ideal reconsidered. *Journal of the American Medical Association* 227:1288–94.

————. 1976a. Philosophy of medicine: Problematic and potential. *Journal of Medicine and Philosophy* 1:5–31.

————. 1976b. Prescribing and drug ingestion: Symbols and substances. *Drug Intelligence and Clinical Pharmacy* 10:624–30.

Pemberton, L. B. 1971. Diagnosis: ca: should we tell the truth? *Bulletin of the American College of Surgeons*, March issue, pp. 7–13.

Penelhum, T. 1970. *Survival and disembodied existence*. London: Rutledge and Kegan Paul.

Pepper, O. H. P. 1945. A note on the placebo. *American Journal of Pharmacy* 117:409–12.

Percival, T. 1803. *Percival's medical ethics*. Reprint edited by C. T. Leake. Huntington, N.Y.: R. E. Krieger Publishing Co., 1975.

Placebos. 1885. *Medical Record* 27:576–77.

Platt, J. 1972. Beyond freedom and dignity: A revolutionary manifesto. *Center Magazine* 5 (March–April): 34–52.

Polanyi, M. 1958. *Personal knowledge*. Chicago: University of Chicago Press.

Porkert, M. 1979. Chinese medicine: A traditional healing science. In *Ways of health: Holistic approaches to ancient and contemporary medicine*, ed. D. S. Sobel. New York: Harcourt, Brace, Jovanovich.

Powles, J. 1973. On the limitations of modern medicine. *Science, Medicine and Man* 1:1–30.

Putnam, H. 1964. Robots: Machines or artificially created life? *Journal of Philosophy* 61:668–91.

Rabkin, J. G., and Struening, E. L. 1976. Life events, stress, and illness. *Science* 194:1013–20.

Rabkin, M. T. 1973. The needs of patients. *New England Journal of Medicine* 228:1019–20.

Rahe, R. H., et al. 1964. Social stress and illness onset. *Journal of Psychosomatic Research* 8:35.

Ramsey, P. 1970. *The patient as person*. New Haven: Yale University Press.

Rawls, J. 1971. *A theory of justice*. Cambridge, Mass.: Belknap Press.

Reiser, S. J. 1978. Humanism and fact-finding in medicine. *New England Journal of Medicine* 229:950–53.

Rickels, K., and Downing, R. W. 1967. Drug- and placebo-treated neurotic outpatients: Pretreatment levels of manifest anxiety, clinical improvement, and side reactions. *Archives of General Psychiatry* 16:369–72.

Riley, J. N. 1976. Western medicine's attempt to be more scientific. Paper presented before the American Anthropological Association, November 1976, Washington, D.C.

Rosenstock, I. M. 1975. Patients' compliance with health regimens. *Journal of the American Medical Association* 234:402–3.

Rosenthal, D., and Frank, J. D. 1956. Psychotherapy and the placebo effect. *Psychological Bulletin* 53:294–302.

Rosenthal, R. 1963. On the social psychology of the psychological experiment: The experimenter's hypothesis as unintended determinant of the experimental results. *American Scientist* 51:268.

Ryle, G. 1949. *The concept of mind.* London: Hutchinson and Co.

Sackett, D. L. 1978. Patients and therapies: Getting the two together. *New England Journal of Medicine* 298:278–79.

Sandburg, C. 1939. *Abraham Lincoln: The war years.* New York: Charles Scribners Sons.

Shaffer, J. 1965. Recent work on the mind-body problem. *American Philosophical Quarterly* 2:81–104.

———. 1967. Mind-body problem. In *The Encyclopedia of Philosophy,* ed. P. Edwards. New York: Macmillan Co. and Free Press, 5:336–45.

Shapiro, A. K. 1960. A contribution to the history of the placebo effect. *Behavioral Science* 5:109.

———. 1964. Factors contributing to the placebo effect. *American Journal of Psychotherapy.* Supplement 1, 18:73–88.

———. 1968. The placebo response. In *Modern perspectives in world psychiatry,* ed. J. G. Howells. Edinburgh: Oliver and Boyd.

Shapiro, A. K.; Mike, V.; Barten, H.; and Shapiro, E. 1973. Study of the placebo effect with a self-administered placebo test. *Comprehensive Psychiatry* 14:535–48.

Shoemaker, J. V. 1896. *A practical treatise on materia medica and therapeutics.* 4th ed. Philadelphia: F. A. Davis.

Sice, J. 1972. Evaluating medication. *Lancet* 2:651.

Siegler, M., and Osmond, H. 1973. The 'sick role' revisited. *Hastings Center Studies* 1, no. 3, 41–58.

Singer, D. L., and Hurwitz, D. 1967. Long-term experience with sulfonylureas and placebo. *New England Journal of Medicine* 277:450–56.

Skinner, B. F. 1971. *Beyond freedom and dignity.* New York: Alfred A. Knopf.

———. 1974. *About behaviorism.* New York: Alfred A. Knopf.

Sloane, R. B., et al. 1975. Short-term analytically oriented psychotherapy versus behavior therapy. *American Journal of Psychiatry* 132:373–77.

Snow, L. F. 1974. Folk medical beliefs and their implications for the care of patients. *Annals of Internal Medicine* 81:82–96.

Soble, A. 1978. Deception in social science research: Is informed consent possible? *Hastings Center Report* 8 (October): 40–46.

Spicker, S. F., ed. 1970. *The philosophy of the body.* New York: Quadrangle.

Spicker, S. F., and Engelhardt, H. T., Jr., eds. 1976. *Philosophical dimensions of the neuromedical sciences.* Holland: D. Reidel Publishing Co.

Steinbrook, R. M.; Jones, M. B.; and Ainslie, J. D. 1965. Suggestibility and the placebo response. *Journal of Nervous and Mental Disease* 140:87–91.

Stoebel, C. F., and Glueck, B. C. 1973. Biofeedback treatment in medicine and psychiatry: The ultimate placebo? *Seminars in Psychiatry* 5:379–93.

Strawson, P. F. 1958. Persons. In *Minnesota studies in the philosophy of science,* vol. 2, ed. H. Feigl, M. Scriven, and G. Maxwell. Minneapolis: University of Minnesota Press. Reprinted in Chappell (1962).

———. 1968. Freedom and resentment. In *Studies in the philosophy of thought and action,* ed. P. F. Strawson. New York: Oxford University Press.

Tooley, M. 1972. Abortion and infanticide. *Philosophy and Public Affairs* 2:37–65.

Trosko, J. E. 1975–76. On making humane human beings in a garbage-in-garbage-out system. *Interdisciplina* 1 (Winter): 1–25.

Tuke, D. H. 1873. *Illustrations of the influence of the mind upon the body in health and disease.* Philadelphia: Henry C. Lea.

Uhlenhuth, E. H.; Canter, A.; Neustadt, J. O.; and Payson, H. E. 1959. The symptomatic relief of anxiety with meprobamate, phenobarbital and placebo. *American Journal of Psychiatry* 115:905–10.

Veatch, R. M. 1972. Models for ethical medicine in a revolutionary age. *Hastings Center Report* 2 (June): 5–7.

Vickery, D. M., and Fries, J. F. 1976. *Take care of yourself: A consumer's guide to medical care.* Reading, Mass.: Addison-Wesley Publishing Co.

Whitehorn, J. C. 1958. Comment: Psychiatric implications of the placebo effect. *American Journal of Psychiatry* 114: 662–64.

Wiggins, D. 1968. On being in the same place at the same time. *Philosophical Review* 77:90–95.

Wittgenstein, L. 1958. *Philosophical investigations.* Translated by G. E. M. Anscombe. 3d ed. New York: Macmillan Co.

Wolf, S. 1950. Effects of suggestion and conditioning on the action of chemical agents in human subjects—The pharmacology of placebos. *Journal of Clinical Investigation* 29:100–9.

———. 1959. The pharmacology of placebos. *Pharmacological Review* 11:689–704.

Wolf, S., and Pinsky, R. A. 1954. Effects of placebo administration and occurrence of toxic reactions. *Journal of the American Medical Association* 155:339–41.

Wolff, H. G. 1962. A concept of disease in man. *Psychosomatic Medicine* 24:25–30.

Wood, H. C., Jr. 1880. *A treatise on therapeutics, comprising materia medica and toxicology, with especial reference to the application of the physiological action of drugs to clinical medicine.* 3d ed. Philadelphia: J. B. Lippincott and Co.

Worby, C. M., and Babineau, R. 1974. The family interview: Helping patient and family cope with metastatic disease. *Geriatrics* 29:83–94.

Worby, C. M., and Gerard, R. 1978. Family dynamics. In *Family Practice,* ed. R. Rakel, H. Conn, and T. Johnson. 2d ed. Philadelphia: W. B. Saunders.

Index